July, 1963

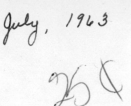

CHEMICAL BONDING AND
THE GEOMETRY OF MOLECULES

Selected Topics in Modern Chemistry

SERIES EDITORS

Professor Harry H. Sisler
Department of Chemistry
University of Florida

Professor Calvin A. VanderWerf
Department of Chemistry
University of Kansas

Published

KIEFFER—*The Mole Concept in Chemistry*
RYSCHKEWITSCH—*Chemical Bonding and the Geometry of Molecules*
SISLER—*Chemistry in Non-Aqueous Solvents*
VANDERWERF—*Acids, Bases, and the Chemistry of the Covalent Bond*

In Press

EYRING and EYRING—*Modern Chemical Kinetics*
OVERMAN—*Basic Concepts of Nuclear Chemistry*
MOELLER—*The Chemistry of the Lanthanides*

(Many additional titles are in preparation.)

Series Editors' Statement

The heart of modern chemistry is the correlation of the properties of substances with the structures of the atoms, molecules, ions, and crystals of which the substances are composed. As chemists have learned more and more concerning the structure of matter and the manner in which the structures of materials determine their properties, the science of chemistry has correspondingly moved steadily from the empiricism of a new and immature discipline toward the deductive character of a well-developed and mature science. For this reason and because of the excellence of Professor Ryschkewitsch's treatment of the subject, we are pleased to present "Chemical Bonding and the Geometry of Molecules" as an important addition to our series SELECTED TOPICS IN MODERN CHEMISTRY.

Professor Ryschkewitsch is a thoroughly sound and intellectually stimulating teacher of general and inorganic chemistry. He brings to his craft, however, not only an excellence in teaching technique, but also the knowledge, experience, and inspiration of a productive, experimental scientist; he is widely known for his research in the chemistry of the derivatives of the hydroborons. Dr. Ryschkewitsch's book proves that not only does he understand the principles of research but also its practical implications. We believe that the student will experience through reading this text some of the spirit of modern chemical research.

Harry H. Sisler
Calvin A. VanderWerf

CHEMICAL BONDING
AND THE GEOMETRY
OF MOLECULES

GEORGE E. RYSCHKEWITSCH

Associate Professor of Chemistry
University of Florida
Gainesville, Florida

New York
REINHOLD PUBLISHING CORPORATION
Chapman & Hall Ltd., London

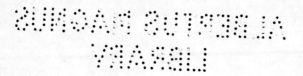
Library of Congress Catalog Card Number: 62-20784
Printed in the United States of America

TO MY READER

The study of the structures of molecules and crystals and their correlation with the properties of substances is one of the central themes of chemistry today. A full understanding of this topic requires an extensive background in mathematics and in quantum mechanics. Therefore, there are those who argue that a discussion of modern structural concepts, detailed enough to allow application to practical chemical problems, should be postponed in the training of a chemistry student until he has acquired sufficient mathematical sophistication to appreciate the details of the theory. This attitude, I feel, places an unnecessary handicap on the inquisitive student. More seriously, the lack of more fundamental knowledge during his early study encourages him to be satisfied with unqualified half truths or, worse, with actually erroneous concepts.

It seems to me that the difficulties of rigorous proof of principles from axioms or the intricacies involved in the quantitative application of the principles to chemical problems should not prevent an open-minded person from accepting these principles without understanding the details of their proof nor from searching for qualitative applications of them.

The author of this book had as his aim giving to the undergraduate chemistry student a plausible exposition of modern thoughts on structural chemistry and placing in his hands some of the conceptual tools which are so helpful in the correlating and understanding of manifold chemical phenomena.

It is the author's hope not only that this end may have been achieved but also that the reader will be able to experience the pleasure of recognizing for himself relations between seemingly unrelated phenomena, because, in the last analysis, it is the disciplined satisfaction of personal curiosity which provides the driving force for the advancement of knowledge.

If this book brings to the student a measure of intellectual stimulation, the author will feel that to a small degree he has repaid his debt to those who trained him, and who encouraged and aided him in writing these pages.

GEORGE E. RYSCHKEWITSCH

Gainesville, Florida
October, 1962

CONTENTS

chapter one _____

ATOMIC STRUCTURE

Chemistry is an experimental science concerned with the composition and properties of matter. The relation of the observed facts to one another forms the basis for the construction of generalized mental pictures, concepts, or models of matter into theories, which ideally should be as simple as possible, so that one can talk conveniently about the multitude of specific facts in a logical manner. Theories can be used to predict the outcome of new experiments. The test of any theory, however, lies in how well these predictions agree with the observed facts.

Modern explanations of the chemical properties of matter are based on well tested concepts of the *atom* and *molecule*. All matter is presumed to consist of exceedingly small fundamental particles (atoms), which retain their identity in all chemical changes. Atoms may form relatively stable combinations with one another (molecules), and chemical changes or reactions involve changes in these molecules. An important part of chemistry, then, is concerned with the questions: "Which combinations of atoms are stable?", "What are the circumstances required for their stability?", and "What conditions make possible the change of one kind of atomic combination into another?" In other words, we ask about the *identity*, the *stability*, and the *reactivity* of molecules.

1

To answer these questions, we will investigate the structure of the atom, and consider whether or not it consists of simpler constituents. If so, how are these components ordered with respect to one another, and what is the nature of the forces that bring about their persistent arrangement?

Constitution of the Atom

Fundamental Particles. In our consideration of the constitution of the atom we will show how certain types of evidence, such as electrolysis, radioactive decay, and the bombardment with helium particles, are inextricably bound up with our present picture of the atom. The first question to be considered concerns the basic constituents of the atom.

In the electrolysis of water, an electric current is passed through this liquid, resulting in the production of hydrogen and oxygen gas. The amount of each of these gases is proportional to the quantity of electrical charge transmitted through the water. Moreover, when substances other than water are electrolyzed by the same quantity of charge, the amounts of change, expressed in moles, stand in a small whole number ratio to one another. This suggests that matter is electrical in nature and that electrical charge is transferred between atoms in discrete units. Indeed, further experiments on the interaction of matter with electricity lead to the discovery that a discrete particle, the electron, is the fundamental carrier of electrical charge. The electron proves to have an exceedingly small mass, even when compared to the lightest atom, and is assigned a negative charge.

If we assume that negatively-charged and very light electrons are present in atoms, we need to ask what carriers of mass and positive charge exist to account for the total weight of atoms and for the fact that matter is, in general, electrically neutral.

Evidence bearing on these points comes from observations on radioactive decay. Two particles of importance can be observed as the result of the disintegration of atoms. One, the proton, carries a charge equal in magnitude to the electronic charge, but of opposite sign and about two thousand times as heavy as the electron. The other, the neutron, is electrically neutral and, of about the same mass as the proton. Thus, two kinds of carriers of mass may exist in atoms, one of which also carries a positive charge. Table 1.1 gives a summary of the properties of the fundamental particles, electron, proton, and neutron.

TABLE 1.1   Fundamental Particles

Particle	Mass (atomic mass units)*	Charge (electronic charge)
Electron	0.00055	-1
Proton	1.00732	$+1$
Neutron	1.00871	0

*One A.M.U. $= 1.66035 \times 10^{-24}$ g.

Distribution of Particles

Granting the existence of these fundamental particles, we still face an important question concerning the distribution and arrangement of particles relative to one another. Are mass and charge uniformly distributed throughout an atom or are they concentrated in certain regions? The answer was found in an ingenious experiment which showed that heavy particles of charged helium atoms were deflected backward on passing through metal foil at high speed. The problem here is quite analogous to a hypothetical instance where one knows the mass and extension of an unseen steel article but wonders whether it is rolled into a uniform sheet so thin that a bullet could pass easily through it, or is manufactured into a picket fence, with massive metal concentrated in bars at certain intervals. Shooting bullets at such a hypothetical object could result in an occasional backward ricochet only if a massive object were occasionally struck head on as would happen in the case of the picket fence. At the atomic level it was found that occasionally the helium particles were deflected backwards; this shows that the mass of the atoms is not uniformly distributed.

Model of the Atom. The composition and distribution of the atom indicated by experimental evidence is consistent with the following model of the atom. The mass is carried almost entirely in a very small positively-charged central region called the nucleus, composed of protons and neutrons. Surrounding the nucleus are negatively-charged electrons, occupying most of the space in the atom. In a neutral atom the positive charge must exactly balance the negative one and therefore the total number of electrons must be equal to the total number of protons in the nucleus. The total number of either of these particles is called the *atomic number* and is equal consequently to the total plus charge on the nucleus or to the total number of electrons in the extranuclear region of a neutral atom. Since the total number of electrons in an atom or a molecule profoundly influences chemical behavior, the atomic numbers form an important basis for the chemical classification of the elements.

The mass of a nucleus is determined by the number of protons plus the number of neutrons which it contains. This sum is termed the *mass number*, and gives the *approximate* mass of the nucleus, since both protons and neutrons have a mass of about 1 A.M.U. The exact mass could be obtained from the sum of the proton and neutron masses if the mass equivalent of the nuclear energy were known.

The masses of atoms are of significance because they determine the weights of atoms and molecules and therefore govern the weight relationships in chemical reactions. Atomic masses, however, do not influence in an important way either the strength or the geometry of chemical bonds. Thus, atoms that differ only in their nuclear masses, but not in their nuclear charge and number of electrons, are essentially chemically equivalent, and form a set of *isotopes*.

Shorthand Notation for Nuclei. In order to facilitate the discussion of nuclei a shorthand notation is often used giving atomic number, mass number, and name of the element in one symbol. Thus $_{30}Zn^{65}$ denotes a zinc nucleus of atomic number 30, denoted by the subscript, and of mass number 65, denoted by the superscript.

Nature of Binding Forces

The final question we asked ourselves at the beginning of this chapter is, "What is the nature of the forces that bring about the persistent arrangement of atoms?" This is difficult to answer in a few sentences. Valuable theories exist describing the binding of protons and neutrons in the nucleus, as well as considerable information on this topic. This field, however, is of little import in chemistry, since atomic nuclei are unchanged in ordinary chemical reactions; chemistry, therefore, does not shed light on nuclear forces and binding energies. However, chemistry is concerned with changes in the arrangement of the extranuclear electrons. The forces that hold these electrons to the nucleus are undoubtedly forces of attraction between positive and negative charges, familiar to us from observations on objects billions of times larger and heavier than electrons. However, the extremely small scale of atomic systems demands a somewhat different method of describing these forces and the energy exhibited in the action of these forces on electrons. This problem will be examined in detail in the next chapter.

Periodic Law

If at this stage we advance the hypothesis that chemical properties are determined by electronic arrangements, it would seem desirable to arrange the elements in the order of increasing atomic numbers and compare the variation of properties of the elements and their compounds in such a series. Under such circumstances, there is a *periodic variation* of properties: similar properties recur after definite intervals. For example, the inert gases helium, neon, argon, krypton, xenon and radon, with atomic numbers 2, 10, 18, 36, 54, and 86, respectively, do not form compounds with other elements under ordinary conditions. The elements lithium, sodium, potassium, rubidium, cesium, and francium with atomic numbers 3, 11, 19, 37, 55, and 87, respectively, again are similar to one another. All are soft metals, react vigorously with water, and, most importantly, form compounds such as LiCl, NaCl, KCl, etc., with the same formula type. Many other properties show such recurring variation. Fig. 1.1 gives a plot of atomic volume *vs.* atomic number that clearly demonstrates a periodicity of upward and downward trends.

Table 1.2 gives an arrangement of the elements by atomic number that also takes into account the periodic variation of properties by grouping similar elements into the same column. The horizontal rows in the table, ending in each case with an inert gas, are called periods. Within a period the atomic number, and therefore the total number of electrons, increases from left to right at the same time that chemical

TABLE 1.2. Periodic Table

$_1$H								
$_3$Li	$_4$Be			Transition Elements				
$_{11}$Na	$_{12}$Mg							
$_{19}$Na	$_{20}$Ca	$_{21}$Sc	$_{22}$Ti	$_{23}$V	$_{24}$Cr	$_{25}$Mn	$_{26}$Fe	$_{27}$Co
$_{37}$Rb	$_{38}$Sr	$_{39}$Y	$_{40}$Zr	$_{41}$Nb*	$_{42}$Mo	$_{43}$Tc*	$_{44}$Ru*	$_{45}$Rh*
$_{55}$Cs	$_{56}$Ba	$_{57}$La	$_{72}$Hf	$_{73}$Ta	$_{74}$W*	$_{75}$Re	$_{76}$Os	$_{77}$Ir
$_{87}$Fr	$_{88}$Ra	$_{89}$Ac						
$_{58}$Ce	$_{59}$Pr	$_{60}$Nd	$_{61}$Pm	$_{62}$Sm	$_{63}$Eu	$_{64}$Gd		
$_{90}$Th	$_{91}$Pa*	$_{92}$U*	$_{93}$Np*	$_{94}$Pu*	$_{95}$Am	$_{96}$Cm*		

*See pp. 26–29.

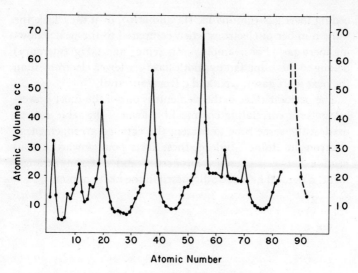

Fig. 1.1. Periodic variation of atomic volume.

properties change profoundly. The vertical columns or groups represent families of elements. As can be seen by inspection of the table, two elements belong to the same family either if they have the same number of electrons in excess of the pre-

					$_5$B	$_6$C	$_7$N	$_8$O	$_9$F	$_{2}$He
										$_{10}$Ne
					$_{13}$Al	$_{14}$Si	$_{15}$P	$_{16}$S	$_{17}$Cl	$_{18}$Ar
$_{28}$Ni	$_{29}$Cu	$_{30}$Zn	$_{31}$Ga	$_{32}$Ge	$_{33}$As	$_{34}$Se	$_{35}$Br	$_{36}$Kr
$_{46}$Pa*	$_{47}$Ag	$_{48}$Cd	$_{49}$In	$_{50}$Sn	$_{51}$Sb	$_{52}$Te	$_{53}$I	$_{54}$Xe
$_{78}$Pt*	$_{79}$Au	$_{80}$Hg	$_{81}$Tl	$_{82}$Pb	$_{83}$Bi	$_{84}$Po	$_{85}$At	$_{86}$Rn

| $_{65}$Tb | $_{66}$Dy | $_{67}$Ho | $_{68}$Er | $_{69}$Tm | $_{70}$Yb | $_{71}$Lu |
| $_{97}$Bk* | $_{98}$Cf* | $_{99}$Es* | $_{100}$Fm* | $_{101}$Md* | $_{102}$No* | $_{103}$Lw |

ceding inert gas (groups Ia, IIa and IIIb), or if they lack the same number of electrons when compared to the next following inert gas. For example, $_{30}$Zn (zinc) and $_{80}$Hg (mercury) belong to the same family; both have six fewer electrons than the next inert gases, $_{36}$Kr and $_{86}$Rn, respectively.

The periodic table of the elements is one of the most powerful tools for correlating chemical behavior. The table can be used at the same time to present the detailed arrangement of electrons in atoms. Indeed, these facts point toward a connection between chemical properties and electron arrangement, a point that will be discussed in the next chapter.

chapter two

ELECTRONIC STRUCTURE
OF THE ATOM

Before a detailed investigation of the relation of electronic structure and chemical behavior is feasible, it is necessary to consider the problem of electronic structure in much the same way that a jeweler might examine a diamond, looking at one facet clearly before inspecting another, checking the relevance or degree of perfection of each, until finally the whole jewel can be comprehended with some intelligence. In this way, the theories and facts that throw light upon electronic structure can be studied one after another, and the aspects of the problem that seem in contradiction, or at least difficult to reconcile, can be placed in a better perspective.

How Pertinent Is Electrostatic Theory?

In view of what has been said about electrons up to now it would be tempting to account for the fact that electrons are held to atoms by using a simple electrostatic theory.

Accordingly, a nucleus with charge Ze would attract an electron with charge e. The force F between these particles can be expressed by means of Coulomb's Law

$$F = \frac{Ze^2}{\epsilon r^2} \qquad 2.1$$

where Z is the atomic number, r is the distance between the nucleus and the electron, and ϵ is unity in a vacuum. The

9

force would be an attractive one and would provide an acceleration on the electron, eventually pulling an originally stationary electron into the nucleus. If the electron were moving, however, the electrostatic attraction would provide a centripetal force holding the electron in an orbit around the nucleus.

The picture would be similar to that of an orbiting satellite, the gravitational pull being replaced by electrostatic attraction.

The electron then would possess potential energy due to its position in the electrostatic field of the nucleus and kinetic energy by virtue of its motion. Its total energy would be the sum of these two energy terms. Designating the electrostatic potential by V, its value can be derived from Coulomb's Law

$$V = - \frac{Ze^2}{r} \qquad\qquad 2.2$$

The kinetic energy of an electron of mass m and velocity v is

$$E_K = \tfrac{1}{2} mv^2 \qquad\qquad 2.3$$

so that the total energy of the electron becomes

$$E_{\text{total}} = V + E_K = - \frac{Ze^2}{r} + \frac{1}{2} mv^2 \qquad\qquad 2.4$$

For a particle moving in a curved path the centripetal force is related in mechanics to the mass, the velocity and the radius of the path by the expression

$$F_{\text{cent.}} = \frac{mv^2}{r} \qquad\qquad 2.5$$

If the electron is to maintain a stable orbit, the electrostatic force and the centripetal force must be the same. Therefore, Eqs. 2.1 and 2.5 give

$$\frac{Ze^2}{r^2} = \frac{mv^2}{r} \qquad\qquad 2.6$$

If both sides of Eq. 2.6 are now multiplied by $r/2$ it is seen that

$$\frac{Ze^2}{2r} = \frac{1}{2} mv^2 \qquad 2.7$$

and from Eqs. 2.2 and 2.3

$$E_K = \frac{Ze^2}{2r} = -\frac{1}{2} V \qquad 2.8$$

Thus the total energy, E, is

$$E = V + E_K = V - \frac{1}{2} V = \frac{1}{2} V$$

and

$$E = -\frac{Ze^2}{2r} \qquad 2.9$$

It is seen from this equation that the energy would tend to become zero when the distance, r, gets infinitely large. At the same time the force also tends to zero according to Eq. 2.1. At finite distances the energy has a negative value while the attractive force has some magnitude. In fact, the smaller r is, the more negative or lower the energy will be. Thus negative values of energy imply stability and therefore this theory seems to account for the stability of electrons in atoms.

However, it is observed in non-atomic systems that charges moving in curved paths give off energy in the form of electromagnetic radiation. This loss of energy would continuously decrease E to a more negative value, therefore, r would have to decrease and eventually the electron would again fall into the nucleus. The situation could be likened to the loss of energy that a satellite would suffer by friction in the upper atmosphere with the consequence of eventual destruction.

There is, for this reason, a very serious objection to the electrostatic theory that makes it necessary to examine more closely the subject of electromagnetic radiation (as it involves atoms).

Electromagnetic Radiation

Electromagnetic radiation is a form of energy. X-radiation, ultraviolet and visible light, radiant heat, and radio waves are examples of this form of energy. The propagation or transfer of this energy through space is most conveniently described in terms of wave motion. The speed of propagation is extremely high, 2.998×10^{-10} cm./sec., the speed of light in a vacuum. The waves of energy are characterized by their wavelength, usually designated by the symbol λ, and their amplitude, a, as indicated in Fig. 2.1.

Fig. 2.1.   Wave motion.

The frequency of the wave motion, v, i.e. the number of vibrations per second, is related to the wavelength by the expression

$$\lambda v = c \qquad 2.10$$

where c is the velocity of light. It is found that radiant energy is transferred to matter in discrete steps, each step involving a *quantum* of light, or *photon*, whose energy is proportional to the frequency of the radiation. This observation forms the basis for the relation between the energy of a photon and the frequency

$$E = hv \qquad 2.11$$

The proportionality constant h has the dimensions of energy times time and has the value of 6.62×10^{-27} erg-sec. It is called Planck's constant and is the same for all types of electromagnetic radiation. Since energy seems to come in discrete units, this quantization thus permits us to view radiation also in terms of particles, the photons. Absorption of photons by atoms would increase their energy by an amount equivalent to $h\upsilon$ per photon.

Atomic Spectra

Let us look now at the opposite process, the release of radiant energy by atomic systems. The process could be symbolized by an equation

$$\text{Atom A}\,(E_1) \rightarrow \text{Atom A}\,(E_2)\, + \,\text{photon}\,(E \,=\, h\upsilon)$$

indicating that energy changes are involved in the process. Since the photon carries away energy in the form of radiation of frequency υ and since energy is conserved in the reaction,

$$E_1 = E_2 + h\upsilon \qquad\qquad 2.12$$
or
$$E_1 - E_2 = h\upsilon$$

Therefore E_1 is larger than E_2 by the amount $h\upsilon$. The emission of radiation from atoms is easily observed, and the study of the frequencies of the radiation emitted therefore gives valuable clues to the energies of atomic systems. For example, in a flame or an electric arc gaseous atoms in a state of relatively high energy (excited states) can be produced. It turns out that such excited states emit light of a color characteristic of the atom when they return to lower energy, producing a *discrete line spectrum*. This means that one observes only radiation with some definite, sharply defined wavelength. Fig. 2.2 gives an illustration of the line spectra of hydrogen and mercury with some of the observed wavelengths.

The existence of discrete atomic spectra leads us to a most important conclusion. To each spectral line of distinct wavelength there corresponds a definite energy $h\nu$. This energy is the difference between the energy of the atom before and after radiation. Since frequencies just a little larger or smaller than ν are not observed, the only plausible inference, apparently, is that *the energies of the atoms themselves have distinct values.* Not all conceivable energies are possible, but only a few, characteristic of the atom. These few give rise in turn to only a few possible combinations of energy differences, and thus to only a few possible wavelengths in the emission of radiation. Thus

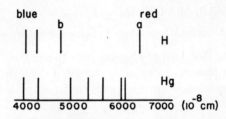

Fig. 2.2. Atomic line spectra.

transitions from one level of energy to the next must occur in sudden jumps of energy instead of a continuous change in energy by infinitesimal increments.

If the energy changes are now identified with changes in electronic energy one can construct from the detailed examination of line spectra electronic energy level diagrams for different atoms or the charged ions derived from them. Fig. 2.3 gives an example of a partial diagram for the hydrogen atom, showing the four lowest levels and the transitions that are possible to these levels from higher ones. These transitions correspond to series of spectral lines named after the

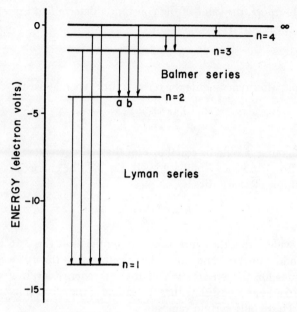

Fig. 2.3. Electronic energy level diagram for the hydrogen atom.

original investigators. The transitions marked *a* and *b* in the Balmer series are responsible for the lines given in Fig. 2.2.

When the deduced energy levels are arranged in the order of increasing energy and are numbered 1,2,3,4, etc. in this order a very interesting relation is found between energy and the corresponding ordinal number n: the product of the energy and square of n is constant

$$n^2E = \text{constant} = a \qquad\qquad 2.13$$

or

$$E = \frac{a}{n^2} \qquad\qquad n = 1,2,3\ldots \qquad 2.14$$

Furthermore, the value of the constant a determined from the data turns out to correspond to

$$a = -\frac{4\pi^2 m Z^2 e^4}{2h^2}$$ 2.15

so that, after rearranging the terms a little, we may write

$$E = -\frac{Ze^2}{2}\left(\frac{1}{n^2}\frac{4\pi^2 m Z e^2}{h^2}\right) \qquad n = 1,2,3\ldots$$ 2.16

Z, of course, would be equal to 1 for the hydrogen atom.

If Eq. 2.16 is now compared with Eq. 2.9, the energy derived by simple electrostatics is

$$E = -\frac{Ze}{2} \cdot \frac{1}{r}$$ 2.9

It is evident that the expression in parenthesis in Eq. 2.16 corresponds to $1/r$, and that the electrostatic theory would account for the observation of discrete energy levels if one would add as a postulate that the radius of the electronic orbit could have only certain values of r.

$$r = n^2 \frac{h^2}{4\pi^2 m Z e^2}$$ 2.17

where n could only be a positive integer. As can be seen from Eq. 2.7, a definite value for r also implies a definite value for v, the velocity of the electron.

This essentially is the postulate of Niels Bohr advanced in 1913 and marks the advent of quantum theory.

This theory did account precisely for the hydrogen spectrum and for the spectra of ions like He^+ or Li^{++} that contain but a single electron, but predicted fewer than the observed number of lines in systems with many electrons. It failed to account for atomic spectra in the presence of a magnetic field and could give no information whatever on the intensities of observed spectral lines.

Quantum Mechanics

A further refinement of the Bohr theory would require the exact and simultaneous measurement of electronic positions and velocities so that corrections to the theory could possibly be inferred from the deviation between theory and experiment. As we shall see, such exact measurements can not be made in principle in the universe as we know it.

Every physical measurement implies that there is an interaction between the object and the measuring device. In the world that we can observe directly with our senses the interactions are often negligibly small compared to what is measured. For example, the position of an object in our field of vision is ascertained if light is reflected from the object and enters our eye. Here there are at least two interactions, one is the impact and scattering of a photon at the object, the other is the absorption of the reflected photon in the retina of the eye, the energy of the photon being converted into a nerve impulse. However, when the weight of the object being studied is very small, say the weight of an electron, the impact and recoil of a photon, small as it is, will cause an appreciable displacement of the electron. As a consequence, the electron will change its speed and direction of travel. Thus, the very act of measuring the position of the electron has produced a change of its velocity. In other words, even the finest probe that can be used, i.e., a beam of photons of light, is too crude a device in view of the small mass of the electron. Subsequent measurements then will contain an error because of the first interference.

By an argument based essentially on this sort of reasoning, W. Heisenberg could relate the error in position due to the measuring process, Δx, to the error in the momentum $\Delta (mv)$ when simultaneous determinations are desired. (The product of mass and velocity is called momentum. Δ signifies a difference, error or uncertainty.) A concise statement of the

Heisenberg Uncertainty Principle is

$$\Delta x \cdot \Delta mv = 2h$$
$$h = 6.6 \times 10^{-27} \text{ erg-sec}$$

2.18

This means that the product of the two errors is never less than twice Planck's constant, even under the most ideal experimental conditions. For sensible objects this limitation on the precision of simultaneous measurements is of no importance, but the small scale of atomic systems causes large percentage errors.

In view of this difficulty, verifiable statements about measured physical quantities cannot be made with unlimited exactness, but always imply an uncertainty. Nevertheless, from a large number of individual measurements one can arrive by statistical analysis at values that have a high probability of being correct and this probability can also be calculated. Properly speaking, then, any distance from the nucleus is possible for the electron; however, some distances are more probable than others and there is also a most probable distance. The discovery of Heisenberg thus forces us into devising a theory that not only makes pertinent predictions but at the same time qualifies these predictions by stating a probability that the expectation is observed.

The impetus to such a theory was given by the suggestion of de Broglie that material particles can behave like waves. This is a parallel to the behavior of energy waves which can behave like streams of particles as was discussed earlier. Experimental verification was soon forthcoming in the observation that beams of electrons are diffracted by passage through matter in much the same fashion as X-rays are. The wavelength corresponding to a particle of matter such as an electron is given by

$$\lambda = \frac{h}{mv}$$

2.19

When Eq. 2.19 was applied to the Bohr atom a most amazing answer was obtained. Combination of Eqs. 2.7 and 2.17 gave, for the electron velocity

$$v = \frac{2\pi \mathcal{Z}e^2 n}{h}$$ 2.20

and substitution into Eq. 2.19 yielded the result

$$\lambda = 2\pi \frac{h^2}{n^2 4\pi^2 m \mathcal{Z}e^2} = 2\pi nr ; n = 1,2..$$ 2.21

This means that the wavelengths associated with an atomic electron are an *integral* multiple of the circumference of the Bohr orbit, $2\pi r$. In fact, Eq. 2.21 represents the condition that a standing wave can be accommodated in the Bohr orbit.

The stage was now set for the full application of the mathematical theory of waves by Heisenberg and, independently, by E. Schroedinger to the description of electrons in atoms. The somewhat mysterious limitation of the radii to only certain values, the postulate of "quantization," stated in Eq. 2.17, could now be understood in terms of standing matter waves. The waves could be described mathematically in much the same fashion as, say, the standing waves in a vibrating violin string. Next the wave equations lend themselves to interpretation in terms of probability. It was thus no longer necessary to make statements concerning electronic motion with a greater precision than experiment could support and the dilemma caused by the Uncertainty Principle was resolved. Finally, the theory was able to make accurate predictions where the Bohr theory had failed.

The theory, called *quantum mechanics* or *wave mechanics*, is now the foundation of the modern description of atomic systems. Mathematically it is quite complex, so that many problems require extensive calculations; many others cannot be solved exactly because our mathematical knowledge is insufficient, but approximate or qualitative answers can be found. In the following we will examine some of the modern conclusions of quantum mechanics.

Orbitals. The interpretation of the wave equation leads to the concept of the *orbital*, replacing the idea of a strictly defined path or orbit for an electron. An orbital is a relatively complicated mathematical expression corresponding to a given electronic energy level which, for each point in space where an electron might be, describes the probability that, in an experiment, the electron will actually be found there. It is difficult to represent an orbital by a simple picture, but Fig. 2.4 attempts to give a comparison between the old and

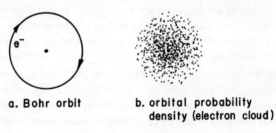

a. Bohr orbit   b. orbital probability
                          density (electron cloud)

Fig. 2.4.   Orbit and orbital.

the new idea. The orbital is represented by a shaded figure, the intensity of the shading corresponding to the relative probability of finding an electron in this particular region. We thus can speak of a probability density or *electron density*, and the picture suggests that in a number of observations the electron behaves as if it were smeared out over the space surrounding the nucleus, as if there were not a solid particle but a diffuse cloud. This *electron cloud* slowly becomes thinner as the distance from the nucleus increases.

ssible Sub-orbitals at Different Principal Levels

$n = 1$	$n = 2$	$n = 3$	$n = 4$
s	s	s	s
	p	p	p
		d	d
			f

e space orbital can accommodate only two
they must have opposite spins. This result is
li's Exclusion Principle. This principle consti-
second restriction on electron distribution, in
quantum conditions.

Electron Configurations

iction, not quite as stringent as the others,
cause of the energies associated with orbitals.
nciple one might state that physical systems

tions of Quantum Numbers and
Capacity of Orbitals

m_l	number of space orbitals	m_s	total number of different electrons
0	1	$\pm\frac{1}{2}$	2
+1	1	$\pm\frac{1}{2}$	2
0	1	$\pm\frac{1}{2}$	2
−1	1	$\pm\frac{1}{2}$	2
	3		6
+2	1	$\pm\frac{1}{2}$	2
+1	1	$\pm\frac{1}{2}$	2
0	1	$\pm\frac{1}{2}$	2
−1	1	$\pm\frac{1}{2}$	2
−2	1	$\pm\frac{1}{2}$	2
	5		10

Three other ways of presenting properties of orbitals
graphically are given in Fig. 2.5. Fig. 2.5a is similar in principle to Fig. 2.5b. The latter graph shows the total relative
density of electrons at a given distance from the nucleus, that
is, the density on a sphere, and the change of density as the

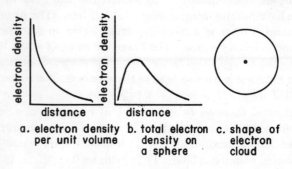

a. electron density per unit volume b. total electron density on a sphere c. shape of electron cloud

Fig. 2.5. Electron distribution plots.

radius of the sphere varies. There is a low probability at very
close distances because in this plot the density per unit volume
is multiplied by the surface area of the sphere and the area of
the sphere decreases rapidly with decreasing radius. The
maximum in the curve corresponds to the distance from the
nucleus where an electron can be located with highest probability. Finally, Fig. 2.5c gives a cross section of the shape
of an electron cloud. In this particular case, (the hydrogen
atom), the electron cloud is spherical with equal density at
equal distances. We shall refer to other shapes shortly.

Quantum Numbers

Four kinds of quantum numbers result from the solutions
of the wave equations. A set of four quantum numbers char-

acterizes each possible atomic orbital. The numbers are also related to the energies associated with different electron distributions in atoms with many electrons.

Principal Quantum Number, n. This number relates to the average distance of the electron from the nucleus and is thus analogous to the number n encountered in the Bohr theory. n can have positive integral values 1,2,3.... etc. The principal quantum number is a most important factor in determining the energy of an electron. The lower the value of n, the lower will be the energy, other factors being the same. Sometimes a letter notation is used instead of the numbers, K standing for $n = 1$, L for $n = 2$, N for $n = 3$, etc.

Azimuthal Quantum Number, l. This quantum number is related to the shape of an orbital. l again can take on integral values but its maximum value is limited by the value of n associated with the orbital. Thus l can be 0, 1, 2....n-1. For example, orbitals with $n = 4$ can have l values of 0, 1, 2 or 3. Thus a principal quantum number of four gives a choice of four different azimuthal quantum numbers. Corresponding letter designations frequently used are s for $l = 0$, p for $l = 1$, d for $l = 2$, f for $l = 3$. Fig. 2.6 gives representations of the shapes of the first three. Once n is fixed, the lower the value of l, the lower will be the energy. Thus s orbitals have lower energies than p orbitals with the same principal quantum number.

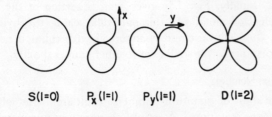

S(l=0)   P$_x$(l=1)   P$_y$(l=1)   D(l=2)

Fig. 2.6.   Orbital shapes.

Magnetic Quantum N
roughly characterizes th
space of the electron clo
and for a given l value
-1, so that the total
For example, there are
for $l = 1$ the magnet
0, or $+1$. These p or
other and are some
directions of extens
energies of orbitals
values of m_l, are th
electric or magneti

Spin Quantum N
the orientation of
with a property
visualized as spi
charged there w
that produced
solenoid. Dep
clockwise or co
opposite direct
of spin, char
or $m_s = -\frac{1}{2}$
acterized by
for arrangen
energy.

Exclusion
quantum
classificati
number
tions ind
exactly th
quantur

TABLE 2.1 Po

$l =$
0
1
2
3

that the sam
electrons and
known as Pau
tutes then a
addition to the

Energy Levels an
A third restr
comes about be
As a general pr

TABLE 2.2 Combina
Electron

letter designation	
s	0
p	1
d	2

will tend to change so that the lowest energy possible is achieved. This state in atoms or molecules is called the ground state and is the most stable state of the system. Under ordinary conditions atoms (and molecules) will be in their lowest possible energy state. The following discussion will be restricted to a consideration of atomic ground states.

The total electronic energy of an atom could be considered as the sum of the energies of individual electrons, each electron contributing an amount appropriate to the orbital that it occupies. Figure 2.7 gives a schematic diagram of electronic energy levels classified by orbitals.

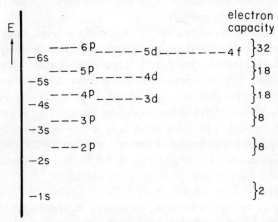

Fig. 2.7. Relative electronic energies.

The prefix number designates the value of n. Each line in the diagram represents one energy level, each can accommodate two electrons of opposite spin. The ground state electron configuration of atoms can now be determined, if the total number of electrons is given. To get the state of minimum energy the first electron would go into the lowest level (1s). After this level has been filled to capacity (2 electrons) the next lowest level would be used (2s), and so on. The process amounts to building up an electron configuration. For example $_7$N would have the configuration $1s^2 2s^2 2p^3$ in the ground state, the superscripts indicating the number of electrons in each sublevel. The total number of electrons, of course, would have to add up to the atomic number for neutral atoms (Z = number of electrons). The general rule is: *energy levels are filled with electrons, starting with the lowest level, each level being filled to capacity before the next higher energy level is used*, in accordance with the order of levels in Fig. 2.7. This gives the electron configuration for atoms or ions in their normal state (ground state, minimum energy).

As can be seen from Fig. 2.7 some of the levels have closely similar energies, and groups of levels with similar energies are separated from each other by larger energy differences. For example, $3s3p$ or $4s3d4p$ or $6s5d4f6p$ form such groups. The diagram also indicates that within a group of energy levels sublevels may have almost the same energy, e.g. 5s and 4d or 6s, 5d and 4f. In these cases it is not possible to make an unequivocal prediction of the electron configuration. $_{23}$V, vanadium, has a configuration $4s^2 3d^3$ for the electrons in the highest energy group while $_{24}$Cr, chromium, has the configuration $4s^1 3d^5$ rather than $4s^2 3d^4$. Again $_{41}$Nb (niobium) with as many electrons as vanadium in the highest energy group, has a configuration $5s^1 4d^4$, leaving the s level only partly filled. Such irregularities are found only when there are different sublevels of almost identical energy. In such cases, the forces that electron distributions in the different sublevels exert on each other become relatively important in determining the configuration of lowest energy.

Table 2.3 gives a summary of the electron configurations of neutral isolated atoms. The table gives in each column the

TABLE 2.3 Outer Electron Configurations of the Atoms

core e	n	ns																	
		ns	1	2	2	2	2	1	2	2	2	2	1	2	2	2	2	2	2	2
		np	—	—	—	—	—	—	—	—	—	—	—	—	1	2	3	4	5	6
		(n-1)d	—	—	1	2	3	5	5	6	7	8	10	10	10	10	10	10	10	10
0	n=1		1H																	2He
2	n=2		3Li	4Be											5B	6C	7N	8O	9F	10Ne
10	n=3		11Na	12Mg											13Al	14Si	15P	16S	17Cl	18Ar
18	n=4		19K	20Ca	21Sc	22Ti	23V	24Cr	25Mn	26Fe	27Co	28Ni	29Cu	30Zn	31Ga	32Ge	33As	34Se	35Br	36Kr
36	n=5		37Rb	38Sr	39Y	40Zr	41Nb*	42Mo*	43Tc*	44Ru*	45Rh*	46Pd*	47Ag	48Cd	49In	50Sn	51Sb	52Te	53I	54Xe
54	n=6		55Cs	56Ba	57La	72Hf	73Ta	74W*	75Re	76Os	77Ir	78Pt*	79Au	80Hg	81Tl	82Pb	83Bi	84Po	85At	86Rn
86	n=7		87Fr	88Ra	89Ac															

Transition Elements (columns 21Sc through 30Zn and their congeners)

core e	n															
		ns	2	2	2	2	2	2	2	2	2	2	2	2	2	2
		(n-1)d	—	—	—	—	—	—	1	—	—	—	—	—	—	1
		(n-2)f	2	3	4	5	6	7	7	9	10	11	12	13	14	14
Lanthanides 54	n=6		58Ce	59Pr	60Nd	61Pm	62Sm	63Eu	64Gd	65Tb	66Dy	67Ho	68Er	69Tm	70Yb	71Lu
Actinides 86	n=7		90Th	91Pa*	92U*	93Np*	94Pu*	95Am	96Cm*	97Bk*	98Cf*	99Es*	100Fm*	101Md*	102No*	103Lw

*See text for exception

configuration for the outer electrons, i.e., for the electrons of highest energy in the atom.

It is apparent that the arrangement by outer electron configuration is the same as for the periodic table (Table 1.2). The periodicity in outer electron configuration is thus the same as the periodicity in chemical or physical properties. Each successive row in the table corresponds to increasing principal quantum numbers for the outer electron levels. The total number of electrons with lower energies (inner electrons or core electrons) are given before each row or period. There are a few exceptions to the configurations given in the headings. These are elements $_{41}$Nb, $_{43}$Tc, $_{44}$Ru, $_{45}$Rh, $_{74}$W, and $_{78}$Pt, which have one less s electron and one more d electron, and palladium, $_{46}$Pd, which has a configuration $4d^{10}$. In the actinide series elements 91 to 94 and 95 to 102 probably have one less f electron which is compensated for by an additional d electron. Finally, there can be no $1p$ electrons in He, because of the restriction of quantum numbers; for the same reason there are no $2d$ electrons in the second row.

The elements are often placed into categories on the basis of their electron configurations: the *transition* elements where d orbitals are being filled and the *lanthanides* and *actinides* where f orbitals are being filled; the remainder of the elements are often termed *representative elements*.

So far the discussion has pertained only to neutral atoms. Simple ions produced from atoms by addition or removal of electrons follow, however, much the same rule. In general, atomic species, whether charged or neutral, have the same electron configuration if they are *isoelectronic* to each other, that is, if they have the same total number of electrons. Thus Ca^{++}, K^+, Cl^- and $S^=$ all have the same number of electrons as argon and all have the configuration $3s^23p^6$ in the last occupied levels. The only exceptions to this rule may occur in the transition elements, the lanthanides or the actinides, where s, d and f orbitals have very similar energies. Here the s electrons are usually removed first in the formation of positive ions. This fact causes positive ions to have configurations different from those of neutral atoms: Fe^{++} is $3d^6$ instead of $4s^1 3d^5$ as in the neutral chromium atom, or gadolinium, $_{64}Gd(6s^2 5d^1 4f^7)$, a lanthanide element, produces Gd^{+++} with a $4f^7$ configuration rather than the $6s^2 4f^5$ arrangement isoelectronic with $_{61}Pm$. But Eu^{++} also has a $4f^7$ configuration, so that for incompletely filled d or f levels isoelectronic positive ions still have the same configuration; only the neutral atoms will differ in such a series.

Electron Spin

Up to now we have discussed configurations only in terms of space orbitals and have not considered arrangement of electron spins. Clearly, the arrangement $2s^2 2p^4$ found in oxygen atoms could have a number of different arrangements of electron spin. Fig. 2.8 illustrates three choices, indicating

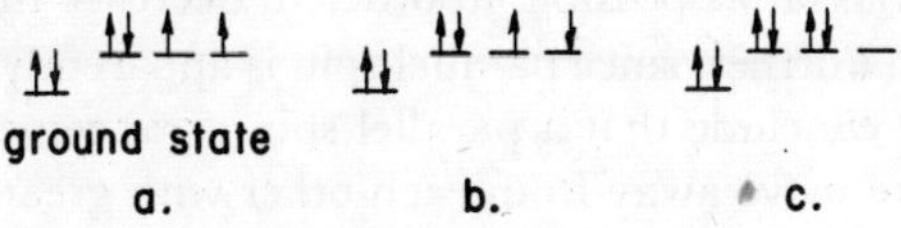

ground state

a.   b.   c.

Fig. 2.8.   Possible spin arrangements.

the two different directions of spin by arrows, $\uparrow$ or $\downarrow$. In both arrangements the $2s$ orbital is completely filled in order to give the minimum energy in accordance with the building-up principle. But the remaining four electrons in the $2p$ orbital could either form two pairs with opposite spins and fill two of the three levels at equal energy (Fig. 2.8c), or they could distribute themselves over all three space orbitals in a pair and two single electrons. In turn the single electrons could have the same spin (parallel spin) or opposed spins (Fig. 2.8a and 2.8b, respectively). The case of parallel spin would confer magnetic properties on the atom due to the two electrons, while opposed spins would cancel each other. Experimentally it is found that the spins are parallel in the ground state, producing the highest possible magnetic moment. The behavior of oxygen is an example of a general rule: *When electrons occupy levels of the same energy in atoms the most stable arrangement is one where the maximum possible number of unpaired electrons are present with parallel spins.* This statement is known as *Hund's rule*.

The maximum number of unpaired electrons is produced when *all* equal-energy orbitals are used. Since each orbital corresponds to a preferred direction in space, electrons apparently prefer to move away from each other when they can do so (without going to a higher energy orbital) rather than pair up in the same region of space (the same space orbital). If one remembers that electrons bear like negative charges it is entirely plausible that they should move away from each other as far as possible in order to decrease their mutual repulsion. Further, since parallel spin is apparently preferred, one might conclude that a parallel spin arrangement enables electrons to move away from each other with greater ease (or higher probability). Quantum mechanical calculations show this to be true.

CHEMICAL BONDING: IONIC COMPOUNDS

With the preceding discussion of the electronic structure of the atom and of electronic energies, the stage has been set to examine the question "Why do atoms combine?" As is well known, the answer to this question is intimately related to the *energy changes* produced when two atoms approach each other. It is therefore worthwhile to study more closely what happens as two atoms come into closer proximity.

Bond Types

Fig. 3.1 gives a schematic plot of the potential energy of two atoms vs. the distance r between the atoms. The significant fact is that, if two atoms are coming closer together, one can distinguish two alternative possibilities: the formation of a stable combination or the failure to combine. In the latter case, the electron clouds of the atoms will interact with each other to produce an increasing repulsion as the distance between the two clouds becomes smaller. This is reflected not only in an increase of the potential energy of the system (as in curve a), but also in the production of an unstable situation. Atoms in such a state would tend to move away from each other, in the direction of lower potential energy, that is, toward infinite separation.

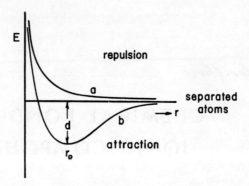

Fig. 3.1. Potential energy curve.

On the other hand, let us take a moment to consider the conditions that lead to the formation of a stable combination. If there is a *net* attraction between atoms, increasing with proximity, the potential energy will decrease as the atoms approach; again the atoms will move towards a lower energy state and will come closer together, as in curve *b*. However, at very small distances the repulsive forces increase much more rapidly than any attractions, since the two inner electron clouds and the two positive nuclei will repel each other strongly, producing, as a consequence, an increase in energy. The net result of this interplay of repulsions and attractions is a region in the potential energy curve where the energy is at a minimum with respect to the separated atoms. The distance at which minimum energy is reached is called the equilibrium internuclear distance, r_o. Motion to either side of r_o will increase the energy. A pair of combining atoms will come together till this minimum is reached and thereafter will vibrate about this position. In order to destroy a stable configuration of minimum energy and again separate the atoms the dissociation energy, *d*, would have to be supplied to the system. d is the difference between the potential energies of the combined atoms and the separated atoms.

It is worth mentioning that this picture of a stable combination, being accompanied by a lowering of potential energy, can be extended to more than two atoms, even though one cannot draw a simple two-dimensional diagram as in Fig. 3.1. Nonetheless, if our attention is focused on this lowering of potential energy, a very fundamental question comes up: "What causes this lowering of energy?"

In broad terms, the energy changes are produced by mutual rearrangements in the electron cloud of one atom under the influence of the other atom. When two atoms are at close proximity the electrons of each atom are not merely attracted to their own individual nucleus but may be drawn also to the nucleus of the other atom. In an extreme case, electrons may even be detached completely and pulled to the other nucleus.

Covalent Bonding. In the first case, attraction of electrons to two atoms, we speak of electron sharing, or *covalent* bonds. An example would be the reaction of gaseous atomic hydrogen to give hydrogen gas with molecules consisting of two hydrogen atoms:

$$H \cdot (g) + H \cdot (g) \rightarrow H{:}H(g) \qquad 3.1$$

where the dots in the symbols represent outer electrons. Here the energy is lowered, since each electron in the molecule, shared between two atoms, is under the influence of two nuclei instead of only one as in the starting atoms. In the description of covalent bonds we shall eventually make extensive use of the orbital concept, and we shall often denote a covalent bond by a line joining the two bonded atoms, for example H—H.

Ionic Bonding. The second case where electrons are detached from one atom and placed on another atom is exemplified by the reaction of *atomic* sodium gas with *atomic* gaseous chlorine to give solid sodium chloride, NaCl. (This is, to be sure, not a common kind of reaction to be carried out, but it is a simple one to discuss.)

$$Na \cdot (g) + Cl \cdot (g) \longrightarrow NaCl(s) \qquad 3.2$$

In the process of this reaction an electron is removed from the sodium atom producing a positively charged sodium ion, and an electron is placed on

$$Na(g) \longrightarrow Na^+(g) + e^- \qquad 3.3$$

the chlorine atom, giving a negatively charged chloride ion. Since the

$$Cl(g) + e^- \longrightarrow Cl^-(g) \qquad 3.4$$

resulting ions have opposite charges they can attract each other and will eventually form an array of many positive and negative ions, that is, solid

$$nNa^+(g) + nCl^-(g) \longrightarrow (NaCl)_n(s) \qquad 3.5$$

sodium chloride. In order to indicate that there is a large, but indefinite, number of Na^+ and Cl^- ions in solid NaCl the subscript n is used in the equation. The lowering of energy here results primarily from the electrostatic attractions between oppositely charged ions. Sodium chloride, then, is held together by *electrovalent* or *ionic* bonds. Both covalent and electrovalent bonding will be discussed in more detail.

Saturation of Bonding. The experimental facts represented in Eqs. 3.1 and 3.2 are worth further consideration because they raise some more significant questions about bonding. In the reaction of atomic hydrogen, H_2 molecules are found, but no molecules with more than two hydrogen atoms are observed. This indicates that there is a definite limit to the ability of atoms to form bonds, that is, there is a saturation of bonding power. In the sodium chloride example a similar situation prevails. No Na^{++} ions are formed, nor are Cl^{--} ions observed, so that again there is a limitation, this time with respect to the number of electrons removed from sodium or the number of electrons that can be placed on chlorine. However, there is no limitation to the number of Na^+—Cl^- pairs that can combine to give solid NaCl.

Ionic Bonding

Composition and Formulas. The composition of ionic compounds is determined by the charges carried on the constituent ions. In a substance composed of oppositely charged particles the total number of positive charges must be equal to the total number of negative charges if the aggregate is to be electrically neutral. For instance, if sodium ion has a +1 charge and chloride ion a − 1 charge, ionic sodium chloride must contain one sodium ion for each chloride so that the charges are balanced. If aluminum ion has a +3 charge and oxide ion a − 2 charge, then three oxide ions with a total of 3 × 2, or six negative charges just balance the combined charge on two aluminum ions. Thus the ratio of the number of aluminum ions to the number of oxide ions in ionic aluminum oxide must be 2:3, and the formula would be Al_2O_3. A knowledge of the charge on ions then is most useful in predicting the composition and formulas of ionic compounds. It should be pointed out, though, that the prediction of a formula does not prove the existence of a particular compound; proof would have to come through the experimental determination of composition.

Ionization Potential. In the formation of ionic solids from atoms we assumed several steps, as follows: first, the detachment of an electron from one atom, producing a positive ion (Eq. 3.3); second, the attachment of an electron to another atom giving a negative ion (Eq. 3.4); finally, the condensation of a large number of positive and negative ions to make an over-all neutral aggregate, the ionic solid (Eq. 3.5). Now we shall take up the changes involved in each of these steps separately.

The energy involved in removing an electron completely from a gaseous atom can be measured directly by a variety of methods. As a matter of fact, a detailed analysis of atomic line spectra can provide this information because complete detachment of an electron corresponds to exciting the electron to an energy level with infinitely large principal quantum number (see Fig. 2.3). The process of producing a gaseous positive ion in its ground state and a separate electron from a ground state atom thus requires the expenditure of energy. The energy involved is called the *first ionization potential*, or ionization energy, of an atom and the process can be represented by

$$\text{1st ionization potential} + A(g) \longrightarrow A^+(g) + e^- \qquad 3.6$$

including the energy requirement in the equation. Of course, it is possible to remove a second electron by supplying enough energy to the positive ion; this energy is called the second ionization potential of A.

$$\text{2nd ionization potential} + A^+(g) \longrightarrow A^{++}(g) + e^- \qquad 3.7$$

The ionization potentials of the elements and many positive ions have been measured. Usually the energies are quoted in electron volts (*ev*), one electron volt corresponding to 1.60×10^{-12} ergs per ion or 23.0 kilocalories per mole of ions. Table 3.1 gives a partial listing of ionization potentials for the elements and their positive ions.

Limitation of Charge. Inspection of the data reveals several important regularities. The first observation is that ionization potentials increase as progressively more electrons are removed from the same atom. Fig. 3.2 gives a diagram of such a variation of successive ionization potentials for beryllium. The

TABLE 3.1   Ionization Potentials of Some Elements

Atomic No.	Element	1st	2nd	3rd	4th	5th
1	H	13.6	...	...	...	...
2	He	24.6	54.4	...	...	...
3	Li	15.4	75.6	122	...	...
4	Be	9.3	18.2	154	218	...
5	B	8.3	25.1	37.9	259	340
6	C	11.3	24.4	47.9	64	392
7	N	14.5	29.6	47.4	77	97
8	O	13.6	35.1	54.9	...	...
9	F	17.4	35.0	62.6	...	...
10	Ne	21.6	41.0	64	...	...
11	Na	5.1	47.3	71.7	...	...
12	Mg	7.6	15.0	80.1	109	...
13	Al	6.0	18.8	28.4	120	154
14	Si	8.1	16.3	33.5	45	167
15	P	11.0	19.7	30.2	...	...
16	S	10.4	23.4	35.0	...	...
17	Cl	13.0	23.8	39.9	...	...
18	Ar	15.8	27.6	40.9	...	...
19	K	4.3	31.8	46	...	...
20	Ca	6.1	11.9	51.2	67	...
37	Rb	4.2	27.4	...	...	...
38	Sr	5.7	11.0	...	...	...
55	Cs	3.9	23.4	...	...	...
56	Ba	5.2	10.0	...	...	...
88	Ra	5.2	10.1	...	...	...

changes are intelligible since the second electron is removed from a positively charged ion instead of from a neutral entity and, therefore, would be bound more strongly than the first. Stated in other words, the electron of highest energy in a positive ion is always lower in energy than the electron of highest energy in the corresponding neutral atom because of the net positive charge. Fig. 3.3 illustrates this point for beryllium.

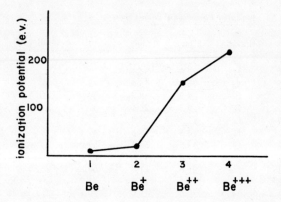

Fig. 3.2.   Ionization potentials of Be.

This is, however, not the only factor serving to increase successive ionization potentials.   As can be seen from Table 3.1 or Fig. 3.2, large jumps in ionization potential do occur; the difference between the second and the third ionization

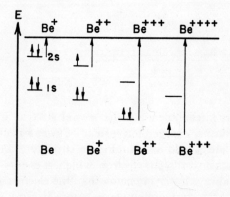

Fig. 3.3.   Ionization potentials and energy levels for Be and its ions.

potential is much larger than the difference between the first and the second. If this were merely the effect of the increasing charge, one would expect an even larger increase between the third and the fourth potential, but this is not so. Why? Reference to Fig. 3.3 provides the explanation. After the removal of two electrons the original Be $(1s^2 2s^2)$ configuration has become $Be^{++}(1s^2)$, isoelectronic with $_2He$. The third electron has to be removed from a low energy $1s$ instead of a $2s$ level. Thus the ionization potential is not only increased because of the increased charge, but *materially* increased because the electron is removed from a level with lower principal quantum number. Table 3.1 quite clearly shows this effect also for other atoms: as soon as an inert gas type configuration is reached, a sudden increase in the ionization potential results. It should be emphasized that this is not due to some mysterious property of the inert gases but to the fact that "inner" or core electrons at much lower energies must now be removed.

This state of affairs has a profound influence on the compositions of ionic compounds for the following reason. In chemical reactions leading to ionic compounds the energy required to produce the positive ion must be supplied by a *release* of energy in another part of the over-all reaction; for instance, the formation of the solid from the ions would provide energy through the action of electrostatic forces. The energy-releasing steps, however, cannot provide more than about twenty-five or thirty electron volts (600–700 kcal/mole) as a maximum. But it is seen in Table 3.1 that the ionization potentials of inert gas configurations are higher than this value (e.g., $Be^{++}(1s^2)$: 154 ev). Therefore the maximum positive charge on a simple ion that can be produced by chemical means is the charge corresponding to an inert gas electron configuration, and this limit is imposed because chemical reactions are limited in the amount of energy available.

This maximum charge is usually attained in ionic compounds of elements immediately following the inert gases in the periodic table. For instance, the alkali metals with a ns^1 outer electron configuration (one more electron than an inert gas) readily lose one electron to form singly charged positive ions. The alkaline earth metals (Be, Mg, Ca, Sr, Ba, Ra) with two more electrons than an inert gas form doubly charged positive ions in ionic compounds. Also in many instances a $+3$ charge is reached on a simple ion with an electron configuration isoelectronic to an inert gas, e.g., $_{13}Al^{+3}$, $_{21}Sc^{+3}$, $_{39}Y^{+3}$ and $_{57}La^{+3}$. However, a simple B^{+3} ion has never been observed in a compound. The explanation for this lies in the fact that the third ionization potential of boron is too high (38 ev) for the production of a $+3$ ion. In this instance, then, "ionic valence" is saturated even before an inert gas configuration is reached because of the increase in ionization potential due to increasing the net charge on the ion. As a matter of fact, one often finds that covalent bonds are formed in preference to ionic bonds in such cases. In the reaction of boron with excess chlorine gas three covalent bonds can be formed in the compound BCl_3 so that the reaction proceeds as

$$2B(s) + 3Cl_2(g) \rightarrow 2BCl_3(g) \qquad 3.8$$

rather than to give an ionic compound

$$B(s) + Cl_2 \rightarrow BCl_2(s) \qquad 3.9$$

where boron has only a $+2$ charge.

In general, it is observed that the charges on *simple* positive ions are limited to a maximum of three even if an inert gas configuration is not reached. Thus the elements of the transition series all may lose two electrons (the *s* electrons are lost first) to give dipositive ions in ionic compounds, and a number of them give $+3$ ions. Similarly, as a rule, the lanthanide elements may lose three electrons to give $+3$ ions. The remaining ions then have incompletely filled d levels (or f levels for lanthanides) but do not reach an inert gas configuration because the subsequent ionization potentials are too high. For example, titanium tetrachloride, $TiCl_4$, on first glance, might be supposed to contain a Ti^{+4} ion for each four Cl^- ions. In view of the preceding discussion, however, the description of $TiCl_4$ in terms of ionic bonding is not adequate because of the high positive charge in Ti. Indeed, $TiCl_4$ exists as discrete molecules and its stability is better accounted for in terms of covalent bonding.

Variation of Ionization Potential in a Period. A further regularity is noted in the variation of ionization potential in a horizontal period. Fig. 3.4 shows a general increase in ioniza-

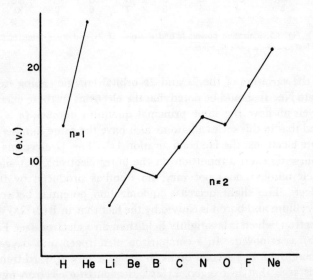

Fig. 3.4. Ionization potential trends in a period.

tion potential as the atomic number increases. This effect can be attributed to the increase in nuclear charge, since a higher charge will produce a larger attraction on the electron, decreasing its energy and making it more difficult to remove the electron from an atom. Fig. 3.5 shows a schematic diagram

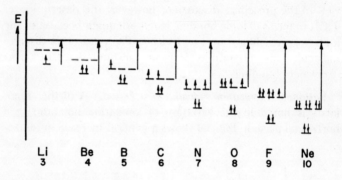

Fig. 3.5. Ionization potentials and energies of 2s and 2p orbitals in the first row of the periodic table.

of the variation of the 2s and 2p orbital energies going from Li to Ne. It should be noted that the electrons in these energy levels all have the same principal quantum number ($n = 2$) and that in this series all atoms also have the same number of core electrons, the He configuration $1s^2$. The 1s electrons of course do exert a repulsion on the outer electrons, but since their number does not vary, no trend is produced by this effect. The slight decrease in ionization potential between beryllium and boron is caused by the fact that in B($2s^2 2p$) a p electron, which is less tightly held than an s electron (see Fig. 3.5), is removed. In a comparison of nitrogen and oxygen, where there is a second break in the generally upward trend, it is seen that in oxygen, $2s^2 2p^4$, the fourth p electron must pair up with another p electron. As was pointed out at the end of Chapter 2, such an arrangement places two electrons into the same region of space, with opposite spin. This causes an increase in energy when compared to nitrogen, $2s^2 2p^3$, where the three p electrons can avoid each other. Fluorine and neon fall in line with oxygen, since in all three cases a paired p electron is removed.

In the second ionization potentials the same upward trend continues from left to right in a period. As a consequence of these trends, positive ions are produced chemically only from elements at the left hand side of the periodic table. The increase in ionization potential towards the right makes positive ion production energetically too expensive. Elements on the right side of the periodic table nevertheless can react, either through the formation of negative ions or of covalent bonds.

Variation of Ionization Potential in a Family. Going down a column in the periodic table, one finds a steady decrease in ionization potential (Fig. 3.6). The decreases from element to

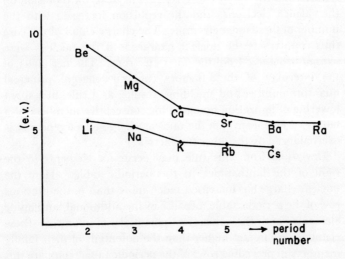

Fig. 3.6. Ionization potential trends in a family.

element are, however, quite small, so that there is relatively little change over the whole family. This fact, by the way, is partly responsible for the similarity in chemical behavior within a family.

A number of opposing factors determine the final values of ionization potentials and their trends. As we go downward within a family there is an increase in nuclear charge. This would tend to lower the electronic energy, and the ionization potential would be expected to increase. But opposing this trend there are two other factors. First, the electron which is lost has a different principal quantum number for each member of the family. In fact, the principal quantum number of the outer electrons increases going down in the family and the electron thus can be removed progressively easier. A second factor which also will facilitate removal of a valence electron is related to the change in the number of core electrons. The core electrons are, on the average, concentrated between the nucleus and the valence electrons. They exert a repulsion on the valence electrons, and the repulsion increases with the number of these inner electrons. The charge cloud of the core thus counteracts the nuclear charge as if the nucleus were *screened* or *shielded* from the outer electrons. The net effect of the interplay of these factors (nuclear charge, principal quantum number and shielding) results, as a rule, in a slight lowering of ionization potential for consecutive members of a family. This means that the nuclear charge effect generally is overbalanced by the other two factors.

Deviations from this rule may occur for elements to the right of the lanthanides in the periodic table. Here the nuclear charge has increased much more than in the previous row of the periodic table, because of the additional lanthanide elements, and the ionization potentials of many of these elements are in fact higher than the potentials of their family members in preceding rows of the periodic table (compare this to the lanthanide contraction, p. 52).

Electron Affinity. In the formation of sodium chloride one of the steps involves the attachment of an electron to a gaseous chlorine atom, producing a chloride ion.

$$Cl(g) + e^- \rightarrow Cl^-(g) \qquad 3.10$$

The production of a negative ion certainly is a general phenomenon in the formation of simple ionic compounds. To be sure, the ions are eventually found in the solid ionic crystal, but it will be profitable to consider briefly the formation of negative ions in the gaseous state. Much less is known about the energy changes involved in the production of gaseous negative ions than about ionization potentials. Table 3.2 gives

TABLE 3.2 Electron Affinities of Some Elements

	E. A. (ev)		E. A. (ev)*
H	0.75	O	-7
F	3.9	S	-3.5
Cl	4.0	Se	-4.2
Br	3.8		
I	3.4		

*For formation of -2 ion.

values for the energy *released* when an electron is attached to a gaseous atom, producing a gaseous ion. This energy quantity is termed the *electron affinity* of the atom. The data show that in hydrogen and the halogen series (F to I) energy is released when a gaseous negative ion is formed, and chloride and fluoride ions are the most easily formed of the halide ions. All the E. A. values quoted in Table 3.2 refer to the production of inert gas type negative ions. If more electrons were added to these ions, leading to a larger net negative charge, the additional electron would then be added to a higher principal quantum number level. This would require without doubt the input of a considerable amount of energy. As a consequence, the process

$$O^{--}(g) + e^- \rightarrow O^{-3}(g) \qquad 3.11$$
$$(2s^2 2p^6) \qquad\qquad (2s^2 2p^6 3s^1)$$

very likely requires so much energy that it cannot be carried out by chemical reactions. As a matter of fact, all attempts to produce negative ions have been in vain where electrons had to be added to an inert gas structure. Thus, the maximum charge on simple negative ions is reached when an inert gas configuration is attained.

As with simple positive ions, there is yet another limitation on the charge that can be carried on a simple negative ion. When two negative charges are placed on an atom, the second electron must be added against the repulsion of the negative charge already on the atom. The result is that energy is absorbed in the process. The addition of a third electron to a doubly charged negative ion requires a still greater amount of energy. As a consequence of this effect, the negative charge on simple ions is limited to a maximum of three units. For instance, Si^{-4} ions are not found in compounds, even though four electrons could be added to silicon $3s^2 3p^2$ before the next higher levels would have to be used. Instead, silicon tends to form molecules with four covalent bonds with a greater or lesser degree of polarity (p. 77) in preference to ionic compounds containing silicide ions with relatively small negative charges. The situation then with negative ions is rather similar to the state of affairs with positive ions, that is, highly charged ions are not formed in chemical processes.

It should be kept in mind that the preceding discussion referred to simple ions, that is, to species containing only one atom. In molecular ions like SO_4^{--}, CO_3^{--}, or PO_4^{-3} the total negative charge can be distributed over several atoms, and repulsions between like charges are reduced. Thus complex negative ions with very high charges may exist if the charged molecule is large and the charges can distribute themselves over the molecule.

Formation of Ionic Solids

Returning again to the formation of sodium chloride it is seen that the formation of a gaseous sodium ion requires an input of 5.1 *ev* to produce $Na^+(g)$, while the formation of $Cl^-(g)$ from atoms releases 4.0 *ev* of energy. The reaction

$$Na(g) + Cl(g) \rightarrow Na^+(g) + Cl^-(g) \qquad 3.12$$

thus used up 5.1 − 4.0, or 1.1 electron volts per sodium atom. The pair of separate gaseous ions has, therefore, a higher energy than a pair of the atoms, and reaction to form these separate ions would not be expected to occur. In general, the potential energy of two ions with positive charge z_+ and negative charge z_-, respectively, with their centers at a distance d from each other, is given by the expression

$$V_{+-} = -\frac{z_+ z_- e^2}{d} \qquad 3.13$$

The ions attracting each other by virtue of their opposite charges may thus decrease their energy if they are allowed to move closer together. According to Eq. 3.13, the most negative or lowest energy would be obtained when the distance reaches zero. But in accordance with Fig. 3.1 repulsive forces will be acting also, since negatively charged electron clouds will start to merge with each other, leading to a minimum energy at some distance d_0. The increase in energy due to this repulsion is not as readily evaluated as the attractive potential because one deals with a distribution of many charges, but it is found experimentally that at the minimum energy the repulsive potential is about 10–15% of the attractive potential (but, of course, opposite in sign), depending on the electron configurations of the ions. For sodium chloride then, the approximate net lowering of energy will be

$$V^{\circ}_{+-} = -\frac{e^2}{d_{\mathrm{o}}}(1 - .15) \qquad\qquad 3.14$$

when an ion pair is formed ($z_+ = 1, z_- = 1$). At the observed equilibrium internuclear distance, the value of the electrostatic energy, about 4.5 *ev*, is sufficient to make the Na^+Cl^- ion pair stable with respect to the gaseous atoms as the starting point.

The actual result of the reaction in Eq. 3.2, however, is the formation of an ionic solid as in Fig. 3.7. Apparently, ion pairs can react further with each other to give an extended orderly array, because the electrostatic force field of a charged particle extends in all directions. The Coulomb ionic attractions cannot be saturated. Fig. 3.8 illustrates the interactions occurring between two ion pairs at close distance. As the atoms come together, the original attractions still exist, while there are two new strong attractive interactions produced, leading to a lowering of energy. Of course in this close

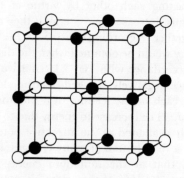

Fig. 3.7. NaCl crystal lattice.

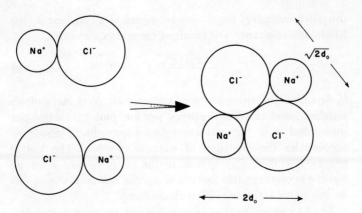

Fig. 3.8. Condensation of two ion pairs into a cluster.

proximity, the ions of like charge also repel each other. The distance through which the repulsions act is, however, greater than the distance through which the attractions act, and the net result is still a lowering of the energy.

A simple calculation will make this point clear. The two new attractions at a distance d_0 give a potential energy of $2V^{\circ}_{+-}$; the repulsions at a distance $\sqrt{2}\, d_0$ give a potential energy with opposite sign of $-2V^{\circ}_{+-} / \sqrt{2}$; the net change then is $2V^{\circ}_{+-} (1 - 1/\sqrt{2}) = 0.6V^{\circ}_{+-}$ for two ion pairs or $0.3V^{\circ}_{+-}$ for each ion pair. A cluster of two ion pairs is thus more stable than two separate ion pairs.

This process of clustering can continue with progressive lowering of energy for each new ion pair added to the cluster. In this sense, ionic bonding power is never saturated in crystals of finite size. The eventual limit of potential energy of a very large crystal is determined only by its geometry, and this limit is reached in practice in crystals that are visible to the naked eye. The geometry factor can be incorporated into the potential energy expression by means of a constant A, the Madelung constant. The resulting general expression is

$$U_o = - \frac{z_+ z_- e^2}{d_o} \mathcal{N}(1 - a)A \qquad 3.15$$

U_o is called the *lattice energy* of the crystal; $\mathcal{N}$ is Avogadro's number, used to convert energy per ion pair to energy per mole, and a is the correction factor introduced above to account for the repulsion of electron clouds. The lattice energy, U_o, then corresponds to the *energy released when the requisite number of positive ions and of negative ions are condensed into an ionic crystal to form one mole of the compound.*

Eq. 3.15 indicates that ionic solids will increase in stability with respect to the gaseous ions as the ionic charge z increases and as the distance between the ions decreases. This is the reason why, say, the compound MgCl does not exist. In this compound Mg^+ ions would be present, and the crystalline solid would not be as stable as the $MgCl_2$ crystal where magnesium ion has two positive charges. The large amount of energy liberated when ionic *solids* are formed from the gaseous ions is the predominant driving force in the production of ionic compounds.

Ionic Size. The size of an ion is a somewhat hazy concept because the modern notion of atoms pictures the electron distribution to extend to infinity. Nevertheless, it is true that there are definite distances established between the centers of atoms in a compound. It is thus natural to attempt to conceive of the distance between, say, Na^+ and Cl^- in solid sodium chloride as being made up as a sum of two contributions, one from the negative ion and the other the positive ion. This amounts to defining the sizes of ions in such a manner that in each ionic compound the sum of the ionic radii equals the observed interionic distance at equilibrium.

$$d_o = r_+ + r_- \qquad 3.16$$

This notion is not unreasonable, because the electron densities drop off rather rapidly with distance so that the bulk of the total electron cloud around an ion is contained in a relatively small space (see Fig. 2.5). Other support for this view comes from the fact that repulsions between electron clouds become strong, and increase rapidly with diminishing distance, only at relatively small distances from the nucleus (see Fig. 3.1). This again means that electron density is predominantly confined to a volume close to the nucleus. It should be observed, though, that the equilibrium distance, d_o, is the result of a balance between repulsions *and* attractions and that therefore d_o will depend to some extent on the attractive energy. It follows, therefore, that ionic sizes depend somewhat on the strength of the bonding. This state of affairs, by the way, complicates the notion of *any* size measure on the atomic scale. Nevertheless, it has been possible to assign to common ions radii in accord with Eq. 3.16, and, fortunately, the radii not only reproduce the interionic distances for the compounds that were used in calculating the radii, but also give relatively accurate predictions for other compounds. Thus experimental data from NaF, KCl, and RbBr may be used to calculate ionic radii for the six ions, and the set of radii so obtained may be used to calculate the interionic distances in NaCl, NaBr, KF, KBr, RbF, and RbCl.

Table 3.3 gives a compilation of ionic radii. It is seen that for isoelectronic ions the radius decreases as the net positive charge increases. In relation to the periodic table this means that ion size decreases from left to right in a period. This is due to the same factors that make the ionization potential increase: electrons are held more tightly and thus move closer to the nucleus. Going down a periodic family, we find that the increasing principal quantum number and the increased screening by core electrons produce an increase in ionic size.

In the transition metal series, adjoining ions, having the same charge, differ from each other by one electron. In spite

TABLE 3.3   Ionic Radii (in A)

A. Inert Gas Type Ions						
electron conf.	−3	−2	−1	+1	+2	+3
He	...	...	H	Li	Be	...
	...	...	2.08	0.60	0.31	...
Ne	N	O	F	Na	Mg	Al
		1.40	1.36	0.95	0.65	0.50
Ar	P	S	Cl	K	Ca	Sc
		1.84	1.81	1.33	0.99	0.81
Kr	As	Se	Br	Rb	Sr	Y
		1.98	1.95	1.48	1.13	0.93
Xe	Sb	Te	I	Cs	Ba	La
	2.45	2.21	2.16	1.69	1.35	1.15

B. Transition Metal Ions (+2 charge)						
Ti	V	Cr	Mn	Fe	Co	Ni
0.90	0.88	0.84	0.80	0.76	0.74	0.72

of the increase in electrons from left to right, there is a decrease in ionic size. Again, as with the ionization potentials, the increasing nuclear charge, at constant principal quantum number, produces a net increase in bonding of the electrons and a corresponding shrinkage in ionic radius.

Lanthanide Contraction. The decrease in ionic size with increasing nuclear charge in a period is especially noteworthy in the last period of the transition metals, starting with $_{57}La^{+3}$. Between $_{57}La$ and $_{72}Hf$ there are fourteen elements, the lanthanides, or rare earth elements. The lanthanides all form ions with a +3 charge and differ in the number of $4f$ (or $5d$) electrons. In this series, there is, of course, a decrease in size resulting from the increase in nuclear charge. However, by the time hafnium has been reached the contraction has become so large that hafnium has about the same size as zirconium, immediately *above* it in the periodic table. This is contrary to the general rule that the lower members of a family are larger in size than the higher ones. Elements following hafnium also are unexpectedly small as a consequence of this so-called *lanthanide contraction*.

The similarity in size causes a very close similarity in chemical properties: hafnium and zirconium compounds occur together in nature and are very difficult to distinguish from each other, and other pairs of elements following zirconium and hafnium resemble each other more closely than is usual for two successive members of a family.

Crystal Geometry. Figs. 3.7 and 3.9 and Table 3.4 give examples of geometries for a number of crystal types. The geometries possible for a given compound are limited by its formula type and by the relative sizes of its ions. A 1:1 compound like NaCl cannot fill the CaF_2 type structure simply because it has only half the requisite number of negative ions and therefore half of the negative ion positions in the CaF_2 lattice would remain empty.

The restrictions on crystal geometry by relative ion sizes are not as severe. Comparing the illustrations of NaCl and CsCl, we see that there is a difference in the number of nearest neighbors that ions have in these structures. In NaCl each ion is surrounded by six other ions of opposite charge, whereas in CsCl each ion has eight nearest neighbors. Finally, in CaF_2,

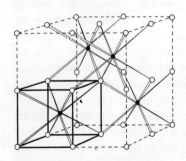

Fig. 3.9a. CsCl lattice.

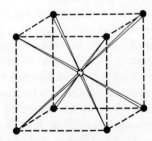

Fig. 3.9b. CaF_2 lattice. Ca^{++} shown as ● and F^- as ○.

TABLE 3.4   Some Crystal Geometries

Structure	Examples	Coord. Nos.	A
Wurtzite	ZnS, AlN, BrO	4	1.641
Rock salt	NaCl, CaO, AgCl, NaH	6	1.748
Caesium chloride	CsCl, TlCl, LiHg, CsCN	8	1.763
β-Quartz	SiO_2, GeO_2	2,4	2.220
Rutile	TiO_2, MgF_2	3,6	2.408
Fluorite	CaF_2, $SrCl_2$, Na_2O	4,8	2.519
Corundum	Al_2O_3, Fe_2O_3, Cr_2O_3	4,6	4.172

Ca^{++} is surrounded by eight F^- and each F^- by four Ca^{++}. The number of closest neighbors is called the *coordination number* of the ion.

The effect of coordination number on the Madelung constant, A, and therefore on the lattice energy, is clearly demonstrated in Table 3.4 when same formula types are compared: the larger the coordination number, the larger the value of A. This is due, of course, to the larger number of attractive interactions that are possible. On the whole, though, this variation amounts to only a few per cent of the lattice energy.

Nevertheless, if a structure with a given coordination number is to be stable, there must be enough space around each ion to accommodate all the nearest neighbors. If the central ion is too small, strong repulsions would be produced between large surrounding ions of opposite charge trying to maintain contact with the central ion. The ratio of radii of the positive and negative ions effectively determines the maximum coordination number if strong repulsions are to be avoided, and this radius ratio at which *all* ions are just in contact with each other can be calculated for each coordination number in a straightforward manner from solid geometry. If the radius ratio is much below this critical value, strong repulsion would then sharply decrease the chances that such a structure may exist. Table 3.5 gives a list of these limiting radius ratios.

From these numbers we can readily see why the structures of BeO (Wurtzite, coord. no. 4) and MgO (Rocksalt, coord. no. 6) differ. The Mg:O radius ratio is 0.47, well above the limit of 0.44 for six-coordination; but the Be:O ratio is 0.23 which is just above the limiting value for tetrahedral coordination of four.

Again, KBr does not crystallize with the cesium chloride structure in spite of a higher Madelung constant which would give a more favorable lattice energy. The K:Br radius ratio is 0.68, which is less than the minimum value (0.732) for a stable body-centered cubic arrangement, as in CsCl, with coordination number eight. Even though KBr could form a tetrahedral lattice (Wurtzite) with coordination number four, the lower energy for six-coordination makes the NaCl lattice the preferred structure. Other examples of structural differences in seemingly analogous compounds are apparent from Table 3.4 (NaCl-CsCl, SiO_2-TiO_2, MgF_2-CaF_2).

In general, then, the smaller a positive ion is, the lower will be its coordination number with a given negative ion.

Trends in Lattice Energy. We have seen that the lattice energy of ionic crystals is affected to some extent by the coordination numbers of the ions (Table 3.4) and by repulsion between ions in contact with each other (Eq. 3.14). These factors are, however, of minor importance when compared to the effect of ionic charge and ionic size.

Eq. 3.15 indicates that the larger the charge of the ions, the larger will be the absolute value of the lattice energy, other factors being equal. Table 3.6 gives an illustration of

TABLE 3.5. Limiting Radius Ratios

Coord. No.	Configuration	Limiting Radius Ratios
3	trigonal	.155
4	tetrahedral	.225
6	octahedral	.414
8	cubic	.732

TABLE 3.6. Lattice Energies (kcal/mole)

NaF	−214	CaF$_2$	−618	...	
Na$_2$O	−602	CaO	−841	MgO	−760
RbI	−147	CaCO$_3$	−714	MgCO$_3$	−938

the profound effect of ionic charge in the comparison of NaF, Na$_2$O, CaF$_2$, and CaO, where the interionic distances are about the same (see Table 3.3). The effect of ionic size change is illustrated by the comparison of NaF with RbI and CaO with CaCO$_3$. In both cases the second compound consists of larger ions and the crystals become less stable as indicated by the smaller absolute values of the lattice energy. This is in accord with Eq. 3.15, which predicts a decrease in the absolute value of U_o as the interionic distance is increased.

Applications. Lattice energy relations are extremely important for the understanding of reactions where an ionic solid is either produced or consumed. Examples of reaction types are: vaporization (ionic solid consumed), formation of ionic solid from the elements, dissolution (ionic solid consumed), and thermal decompositions of salts with complex anions. The over-all energy changes involved in these reactions can be analyzed by imagining the reaction to occur in a series of steps, one of these involving the input or release of the lattice energy. We should recall here that negative values for energy changes mean that the product of the reaction is more stable than the starting materials, and further, the more negative the energy change is, the greater will be the stability difference, and the greater will be the tendency for the reaction to occur.

Let us take as an example the formation of alkali metal halides (solid), MX, from the solid metal, M, and one-half mole of gaseous elemental halogen, X$_2$. Indicating the energy change associated with this reaction by Q, one may write

$$M(s) + 1/2X_2(g) \xrightarrow{Q} MX(s)$$

This reaction may be broken down into several steps, starting by subliming the solid metal to give a gas, and then removing an electron from the gaseous metal atoms to give the positive ion. The heat of sublimation, S, and the energy corresponding to the ionization potential, I, would have to be supplied to make this possible.

$$M(s) \xrightarrow{S} M(g) \xrightarrow{I} M^+(g) + e^-$$

In turn, the halogen molecules may be dissociated into atoms, supplying one-half the dissociation energy, D, and an electron may be placed on the atom, releasing the energy corresponding to the electron affinity, E.

$$\tfrac{1}{2}X_2(g) \xrightarrow{\tfrac{1}{2}D} X(g) \xrightarrow[+e^-]{E} X^-(g)$$

Finally, the ions may now come together to form the solid and will release the lattice energy U_o.

$$M^+(g) + X^-(g) \xrightarrow{U_o} MX(s)$$

Thus the stepwise process leads to the same final result, as the direct process and the sum of the energy changes in the separate steps should be the same as the direct energy change.

$$M(s) \xrightarrow{S} M(g) \xrightarrow{I} M^+(g)$$
$$+ \qquad\qquad\qquad\qquad\qquad U_o \qquad \longrightarrow MX(s)$$
$$\tfrac{1}{2}X_2(g) \xrightarrow{\tfrac{1}{2}D} X(g) \xrightarrow[Q]{E} X^-(g)$$

and $Q = \tfrac{1}{2}D + E + S + I + U_o$. \qquad 3.17

The diagram is an example of an *energy cycle*, specifically, the *Born-Haber* cycle. We can use the energy equation (Eq. 3.17) derived from it to discuss, for instance, the trends in the heats of formation of alkali metal fluorides and chlorides. It is seen from the Q values in Table 3.7 that the fluorides become less stable going down in a family, whereas the chlorides show the opposite trend. Why?

TABLE 3.7.   Heats of Formation and Lattice Energies of Alkali Metal Halides*

	Fluorides				Chlorides		
	$S + I$	$-Q$	$-U_o$	$\frac{1}{2}D - E$	$-Q$	$-U_o$	$\frac{1}{2}D - E$
Li	162.1	144.7	240.5	-66.3	97.5	196.0	-63.6
Na	144.0	136.6	214.3	-66.3	98.5	178.6	-63.6
K	121.3	134.5	189.5	-66.3	104.9	162.6	-63.6
Rb	115.8	132.8	182.3	-66.3	104.9	157.1	-63.6
Cs	108.5	131.5	173.7	-66.3	106.6	151.5	-63.6
Total change	53.6		66.3			44.5	

*All energies in kcal

The trend in Q for a given halide series is produced by a decrease in $S + I$, and an *opposing* change in U_o. In both series the absolute value of the lattice energy decreases because of the increase in size of the alkali metal ions. Now, the fluorides change much more than the chlorides because a given change in the size of the positive ion produces a proportionately larger difference in the interionic distance when the negative ion is small, as is the case for F^-. Thus the lattice energy change is the predominant influence in setting the trend of the heat of formation of the fluoride, whereas the changes in heats of sublimation and ionization potential determine the trend for the chlorides.

General trends in solubilities of salts can also be understood by a similar analysis in which a general energy cycle is employed.

$$M_aY_b(s) \xrightarrow{-U_o} \begin{array}{c} aM^{+b}(g) \xrightarrow{aH_+} aM^{+b}(aq.) \\ \\ bY^{+a}(g) \xrightarrow{bH_-} bY^{+a}(aq.) \end{array}$$

$$Q_s$$

where Q_s refers to the heat change on dissolution and H to the heat change on hydrating one mole of positive or negative ions respectively. Other factors being equal, the more heat is released on solution the more soluble the compound will be. From the energy relation it is apparent that a large

$$Q_s = -U_o + aH_+ + bH_- \qquad 3.18$$

negative value of the lattice energy (stable crystal) tends to give a positive value of Q_s. This would hinder dissolution and would lead to low solubility.

Accordingly, many fluorides (small ion, large U_o) tend to be less soluble than chlorides; compounds with singly charged ions (low U_o), like alkali metal salts, halides, nitrates, perchlorates, etc., are in general more soluble than compounds with multiply charged ions like alkaline earth salts, carbonates, sulfates, oxalates, phosphates, and silicates. The increase in solubility of the alkaline earth hydroxides with increasing size when going from Be to Ba also follows the trend in lattice energy. In strict comparisons, though, one will also have to take account of variations in the hydration energies.

Finally, let us consider the decomposition of a metal carbonate, MCO_3, to carbon dioxide and metal oxide

$$MCO_3(s) \xrightarrow{-U_R} M^{++}(g) + CO_3^=(g) \xrightarrow[Q_D]{D} M^{++}(g) + O^=(g) +$$

$$CO_2(g) \xrightarrow{U_P} MO(s) + CO_2(g)$$

$$Q_D = D - U_R + U_P$$

where Q_D, the heat change on decomposition, is composed of the heat required to dissociate $CO_3^=$ into $O^=$ and CO_2 and the difference in lattice energies of oxide and carbonate, $U_P - U_R$, the difference being negative because of the smaller size of $O^=$. As in the fluoride vs. chloride comparison on p. 58, the smaller the positive ion is, the larger the effect will be on the lattice energy when the size of the negative ion is changed going from carbonate to oxide. Thus $U_P - U_R$ should be more negative, and Q_D more negative for a smaller positive ion. A carbonate, then, should decompose most readily when the positive ion is smallest because less energy input is required.

This prediction is indeed correct. Consider, e.g., the alkaline earth carbonates, where a regular increase in thermal stability is observed going down the alkaline earth family (increasing size of the cation) and progressively higher decomposition temperatures are required for this series of compounds (Table 3.8).

TABLE 3.8   Decomposition Temperatures for the Reaction
$$MCO_3 \text{ (s)} \longrightarrow MO \text{ (s)} + CO_2 \text{ (g)}$$

MCO_3	$MgCO_3$	$CaCO_3$	$SrCO_3$	$BaCO_3$
Temperature, °C	350	547	778	998

A similar reasoning may be applied to a variety of other decompositions, e.g.,

$$MSO_4(s) \rightarrow MO(s) + SO_3(g)$$
$$M(OH)_2(s) \rightarrow MO(s) + H_2O(g)$$
$$MBF_4(s) \rightarrow MF(s) + BF_3(g)$$

In all these cases the salt with the smallest positive ion shows the lowest thermal stability.

chapter four _____

CHEMICAL BONDING:
COVALENT COMPOUNDS

As we pointed out in Chapter 3, rearrangements in electron distribution can lead to bonding, but these changes do not need to be so extreme as to cause complete shifts of electrons from one atom to the other. In fact, these shifts can result in sharing of one or more electron pairs between two atoms so as to form a covalent bond. The strength of the bond corresponds to the lowering of the energy that results when the atoms come together. The decrease in energy is caused by the additional attraction exerted on an electron when it is in the region of space between *two* atoms and in close proximity to both of them. Thus the problem of assessing the energy of a covalent bond is in essence quite similàr to the problem of calculating the energy of electrons in an atom, except that two nuclear centers have to be considered instead of one. Although this fact seems elementary enough, it actually advances our argument considerably. Now, we can properly speak of *molecular orbitals* in the consideration of electron distributions in molecules, instead of limiting ourselves entirely to electron distributions in atoms.

As in the various atomic space orbitals, there are different geometries of electron clouds in the various molecular orbitals.

Furthermore, as in atomic orbitals, electrons occupy molecular orbitals in pairs, the electrons having opposite spin. Electrons are thus shared, as a rule, in pairs, and we might speak of a covalent bond as an *electron-pair bond*.

In this chapter we shall examine first a convenient way to represent covalent bonds on paper and then discuss the factors that determine the composition of molecules, the extent of electron sharing, the strength of bonding, and the geometry of molecules.

Overlap of Orbitals

The simplest electron-pair bond is the bond between two hydrogen atoms in a hydrogen molecule. In the hydrogen molecule there are two protons and two electrons, giving a neutral entity. Let us look first at the components of this molecule and consider what happens when some of them are brought together.

Consider the interaction of a hydrogen atom and an electron. When an electron is added to a hydrogen atom

$$\text{H} \cdot (g) + e^- \longrightarrow \text{H} :^- (g) + 0.74 \, ev \qquad 4.1$$

there is liberated 0.74 *ev* of energy (see electron affinity, p. 45). The release of energy implies that a proton has the capacity to accommodate one pair of electrons and produce a stable entity. On the other hand, consider the interaction between a hydrogen atom and a proton. As the two approach, again energy is released because in the region between the two protons both nuclei attract the electron and the electron can reside on both atoms. If now a proton *and* an electron are approaching the hydrogen atom, it is not surprising that again energy is released, leaving the system with lower energy and in a more stable state. As a result of this latter interaction a pair of electrons is shared between two protons, releasing 4.72 *ev*.

$$\text{H} \cdot (g) + \text{H} \cdot (g) \longrightarrow \text{H} : \text{H}(g) + 4.72 \, ev \qquad 4.2$$

How can the idea of electron sharing be linked to our concept of atoms? Let us recall that for each atomic space orbital there is a corresponding region in space where there is a high probability of accommodating a pair of electrons (with opposite spins). When two hydrogen atoms with $1s$ orbitals approach each other under such conditions, their orbitals will interpenetrate or overlap. Thus, in the region between the two protons, electron density is reinforced and the resulting combined electron cloud reaches over both atoms. In fact, primarily because of the increased attraction from both nuclei, more electron density is concentrated between atoms than there would be in a simple superposition of electron clouds. In this sense, both electrons are shared between the two atoms and one might represent the molecular orbital as the result of the overlapping combination of two atomic orbitals, one orbital from each atom. In a normal covalent bond this molecular orbital contains a pair of electrons.

The process will, however, not lead to a complete merging of the atoms because there are also repulsive forces acting. The reasons for this are that first, the two positively charged nuclei repel each other, and second, there are also interelectronic repulsions. Both repulsions become very pronounced when the distance between the two atoms is very small so that again a balance is struck between attraction and repulsion to give minimum energy, as in Fig. 4.1.

This description of a covalent bond in terms of overlapping atomic orbitals stems from the desire to retain and use the atomic orbital concept. Atomic orbitals were designed to describe electron distributions in isolated atoms; however, one might expect distortions of the isolated atom electron cloud when it is in close proximity to the positive charge of another atom. A more detailed description of the covalent bond would have to include this distortion.

Since the energy lowering is thought of as resulting from

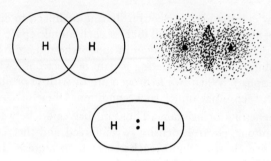

Fig. 4.1. Overlap of orbitals.

orbital overlap, the most effective bonding would be produced by the greatest overlap of orbitals. But the electron density in an orbital drops off very rapidly with increasing distance from the positive center (Fig. 2.5). This means that the atoms must be very close to each other to form a bond effectively. Also, in the case of orbitals with preferred directions (*p* or *d* orbitals), there must be proper alignment of orbitals to produce maximum overlap.

The conditions of short range, dependence on direction, and overlap of orbitals provide a major distinction between covalent and ionic bonding. It was pointed out in Chapter 3 that Coulomb forces between ions act over long distances, act equally in all directions, and are not saturated even in over-all neutral ion aggregates. Covalent bond forces in contrast are significant at short range only and depend on direction, because of the overlap requirement. An electron pair cannot normally be used to form more than one covalent bond. Covalent bond forces thus can be saturated, and only a limited number of bonds can be formed by one atom.

As a consequence, there exist discrete covalently bonded molecules, neutral or with a net charge, that are composed only of a few atoms. Even in the solid state, the molecular groupings commonly preserve their identity. Individual sugar molecules can be distinguished in sugar crystals, whereas it is impossible to see individual ion pairs in an ionic crystal such as sodium chloride.

As we have seen, each covalent bond requires one pair of electrons and a pair of overlapping orbitals, each orbital coming from one of the atoms that are partners in the bond. Thus, one might write formally

orbital (atom 1) + orbital (atom 2) + electron pair $\longrightarrow$

covalent bond   4.3

In general, not all electrons are used in bond formation, so that some non-bonding electron pairs still might occupy a single orbital. These are called *lone* or *unshared pairs*. This could be expressed formally

orbital (atom 1) + electron pair $\longrightarrow$ lone pair (atom 1)   4.4

The electrons of concern to us again are the highest energy electrons (valence electrons), that is, ns, np, and possibly $(n-1)d$ electrons where n is the principal quantum number. In fact, only s and p electrons need to be considered for the representative elements (elements with either completely full or completely empty d levels). Core electrons cannot be used effectively in bonding because they are bound too strongly to their own atoms and therefore cannot be withdrawn effectively into the bonding region; they contribute only slight repulsions to the over-all bonding picture. Since the core electrons also completely fill the inner orbitals, these orbitals are also eliminated from consideration for bonding. Table 4.1 gives a listing of some representative elements, indicating by dots the s and p electrons available. It is seen that the total number of these electrons correspond to the periodic group numbers of these elements.

TABLE 4.1. Electron Dot Formulas for Some Representative Elements

Group	III	IV	V	VI	VII	VIII
No. of Electrons	3	4	5	6	7	8
	·B·	·Ċ·	·N̈·	:Ö·	:F̈·	:N̈e:
	·Al·	·Si·	·P̈·	:S̈·	:C̈l·	:Är:
	·Ga·	·Ge·	·Äs·	:S̈e·	:B̈r·	:K̈r:
	·In·	·Sn·	·Sb·	:Te·	:Ï·	:Xe:
	·Tl·	·Pb·	·Bï·			

The orbitals capable of participating in covalent bonding
must have enough extension in space so that they can overlap
effectively with orbitals from other atoms. Furthermore, their
energies must be relatively low if there is to be a net gain in
stability on overlap. Fig. 4.2 illustrates this point for hydrogen
using 1s and 2s orbitals. Overlap of either two 1s orbitals or
two 2s orbitals will produce a lowering of energy. In the
hydrogen molecule the electron will of course go to the lowest
energy state, and this is produced by overlap of the low energy

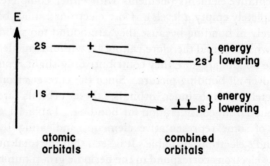

Fig. 4.2. Combination of high energy or low energy orbitals.

$1s$ orbitals. As a general rule, the set of orbitals that can be used in bonding must have energies similar to the energies of atomic orbitals occupied by valence electrons. Hydrogen has only one orbital available in this category, the $1s$ orbital, and thus can form only one covalent bond. The other representative elements may all use one s and three p orbitals at the outer electron level because s and p orbitals with the same principal quantum number have similar energies. The availability of orbitals severely limits the number of covalent bonds that can be formed to each atom, because each covalent bond uses up one orbital.

Electron Octets. The preceding discussion forms the basis for the so-called *octet rule*, which applies strictly only to the elements in the period following helium in the periodic table. The octet rule states that electron sharing may continue till a maximum of eight electrons, or four pairs, surround an atom. In hydrogen, sharing is, of course, limited to one pair. The application of this rule is best illustrated with a few examples, using "electron dot formulas" to give an account of the electrons.

Fluorine gas consists of molecules with two fluorine atoms. Each fluorine atom has seven outer electrons, and the formation of a molecule can then be represented as

$$:\overset{..}{\text{F}}\cdot \; + \; \cdot\overset{..}{\text{F}}: \; \longrightarrow \; :\overset{..}{\underset{..}{\text{F}}}:\overset{..}{\underset{..}{\text{F}}}: \qquad\qquad 4.5$$

indicating that one covalent bond is formed. It is seen that each fluorine atom is surrounded by four pairs of electrons, one pair in the bond, and three unshared pairs on each atom. The four available orbitals on each fluorine are also all occupied, three orbitals accommodating the unshared pairs and the fourth the bonding pair.

Further bond formation by the fluorine molecule is not observed; we can interpret this by considering the hypothetical molecule F_3 with a total of twenty one electrons, produced by adding another fluorine atom to the F_2 molecule

$$:\overset{..}{\underset{..}{F}}:\overset{..}{\underset{..}{F}}:\overset{..}{\underset{..}{F}}:\cdot \qquad\qquad 4.6$$

Here the central fluorine atom would have two bonds. But the fluorine atom on the right has an electron beyond the octet, and this would require an additional orbital beyond the available four. The bonding capacity of fluorine is thus saturated when the F_2 molecule is formed.

Again, consider the fluoroform molecule, CHF_3. Here the four orbitals and four electrons on carbon can form four covalent bonds, one to hydrogen and three to the three fluorine atoms. Again carbon and fluorine have a

$$\cdot\overset{.}{\underset{.}{C}}\cdot \; + \; H\cdot \; + \; 3:\overset{..}{\underset{..}{F}}\cdot \; - \; H:\overset{\overset{\textstyle :\overset{..}{F}:}{}}{\underset{\underset{\textstyle :\overset{..}{\underset{..}{F}}:}{}}{C}}:\overset{..}{\underset{..}{F}}: \qquad 4.7$$

complete octet, using all their orbitals and all electrons.

In water, H_2O, oxygen contributes six electrons and each of the hydrogens one electron, making a total of eight. Each bond uses up a pair, a hydrogen orbital, and an oxygen orbital. The remaining two pairs just can be accommodated in the remaining two oxygen orbitals, to complete an octet.

$$\begin{array}{c} H:\overset{..}{\underset{..}{O}}: \\ H \end{array}$$

Charged species can be described in the same fashion. The hydroxide ion, OH^-, is represented by

$$[:\overset{..}{\underset{..}{O}}: H]^-$$

The negative net charge represents the excess of one electron over the total of seven electrons contributed by a neutral oxygen and a neutral hydrogen atom.

In terms of these examples one can now understand why the inert gases are chemically so unreactive. Their electron configurations have all orbitals filled with pairs so that no more electrons can be accommodated in stable orbitals.

Incomplete Octets. Even though the formation of the maximum number of covalent bonds is a powerful driving force in the formation of molecules, there are instances of molecules where not all of the available orbitals are used. This then will lead to structures where less than four electron pairs surround an atom.

Examples of this kind are most often found in compounds of the boron family, group III of the periodic table.

$$\begin{matrix} & : \overset{..}{C}l : & & CH_3 & & H \\ : \overset{..}{C}l : \overset{..}{B} : \overset{..}{C}l : & & H_3C : \overset{..}{G}a : CH_3 & & \cdot CH_3 = H : \overset{..}{C} : H \end{matrix}$$

    boron trichloride   trimethyl gallium   methyl radical

Examples from other families in the periodic table are diethyl beryllium

$$\begin{matrix} & & & & & & H \;\; H \\ H_5C_2 : Be : C_2H_5 & & \text{where} & & C_2H_5 = & \cdot \overset{..}{C} : \overset{..}{C} : H \\ & & & & & H \;\; H \end{matrix}$$

    diethyl beryllium   ethyl radical

and possibly sulfur (VI) oxide, or sulfur trioxide, SO_3.

$$\begin{matrix} & : \overset{..}{O} : \\ : \overset{..}{O} : \overset{..}{S} : \overset{..}{O} : \end{matrix}$$

Sometimes molecular species with incomplete octets are encountered as intermediate products in complex chemical reactions, as, for example, the methyl carbonium ion,

$$\begin{array}{cc} \overset{\displaystyle H}{H:\overset{\displaystyle \cdot}{\underset{\displaystyle \cdot\cdot}{C}}:H} & + \end{array}$$

The fact that compounds containing this ion are extremely difficult to prepare and keep without further reaction is evidence for great reactivity. This can be explained in terms of the empty orbital—a place where a fourth covalent bond could be formed. Reactions of this type will be discussed a little later.

Expansion of Octet. The octet rule strictly applies to those elements that have only four orbitals available. In those cases, a maximum of four bonds can be formed through overlap. There are, however, a number of molecules where five or six covalent bonds are formed to a central atom. Such behavior is exhibited by elements in the third period and subsequent periods of the periodic table, but never by elements in the second row of the periodic table. A few molecules of this type are listed below.

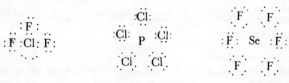

chlorine (III) fluoride phosphorus (V) chloride selenium (VI) fluoride
chlorine trifluoride phosphorus pentachloride selenium hexafluoride

How can this be accounted for by the orbital overlap picture? Obviously, there must be more than four orbitals available in order for more than four covalent bonds to be formed. Inspection of the electronic energy level diagram, Fig. 2.7, shows that for phosphorus the next higher energy orbitals above the $3p$ levels are $4s$ orbitals or $3d$ orbitals. It can be demonstrated by calculation that d orbitals would overlap more effectively than s orbitals because of their greater extension into space (see Fig. 2.6). Covalent bonding in PCl_5 or SeF_6 thus can be accounted for if one assumes that one or two d orbitals can take part in the overlap. Since there are no $2d$ orbitals, second period elements do not have this bonding possibility, and one would not expect such molecules as NCl_5 or OF_6 to be stable. This is in accord with the facts.

As a general rule, then, elements in the third and subsequent periods may use up to two extra d orbitals in bonding. That means that up to six covalent bonds can be formed and up to twelve electrons may surround these atoms in their compounds. In these cases, therefore, the octet rule does not necessarily apply.

It is true, though, that there are many molecules involving elements from the third or subsequent periods with only four electron pairs around the central atom. The difference between these and analogous second row compounds would be that further reaction using the extra d orbitals is a definite possibility. This difference is illustrated by Eqs. 4.8 and 4.9.

$$: NCl_3 + Cl_2 \rightarrow \text{no reaction} \qquad 4.8$$

but

$$: PCl_3 + Cl_2 \rightarrow PCl_5 \qquad 4.9$$

Electron Pair Donation. In the examples cited so far, it could be imagined that each atom contributed one electron to the bond. This assumption is not necessary. As a matter of fact, it does not make any difference in which way the bond is *imagined* to be formed. A water molecule is a stable entity whether it is formed by the union of two hydrogen atoms and an oxygen atom, or whether it is formed by the reaction of two protons with an oxide ion.

$$H \cdot + \cdot \ddot{O} \cdot + \cdot H \rightarrow H : \ddot{O} : H \qquad 4.10$$

or

$$H^+ + :\overset{=}{\underset{..}{O}}: + H^+ \rightarrow H:\underset{..}{O}:H \qquad 4.11$$

In Eq. 4.11 the bond is formed by the union of a proton with an available empty orbital, an oxygen orbital, and a lone pair on oxygen, both electrons being supplied by the oxide ion. The net result is the same: the formation of two stable covalent bonds.

Empty orbitals in atomic or molecular species often represent a point of reactivity with other molecules or atoms that can supply an unshared pair, because the formal conditions for covalent bond formation are met (two orbitals plus an electron pair, Eq. 4.3). The oxygen atom in water, for example, carries two lone, unshared electron pairs. One of these pairs can be used for further bond formation with species that have an empty orbital, like H^+

$$H^+ + :\underset{\underset{H}{..}}{O}:H \rightarrow H:\underset{\underset{H}{..}}{O}:H^+ \qquad 4.12$$

The resulting entity, the hydronium ion, carries a net positive charge. The driving force for the reaction is provided by the fact that a new covalent bond can be formed without materially interfering with the other bonds in the system.

Other examples of this reaction type are the addition of ammonia to boron trichloride

$$\begin{array}{ccc} H & :\overset{..}{\underset{..}{Cl}}: & \\ H:\overset{..}{\underset{H}{N}}: + & B:\overset{..}{\underset{..}{Cl}}: \rightarrow \\ H & :\overset{..}{\underset{..}{Cl}}: & \end{array} \quad \begin{array}{c} H :\overset{..}{\underset{..}{Cl}}: \\ H:N : B:\overset{..}{\underset{..}{Cl}}: \\ H :\overset{..}{\underset{..}{Cl}}: \end{array} \qquad 4.13$$

or the reaction of sulfur (VI) oxide (sulfur trioxide) with hydroxide ion

$$\overset{..}{\underset{..}{:O:}} \quad\quad\quad\quad \overset{..}{\underset{..}{:O:}} \;^-$$
$$:\overset{..}{O}:\overset{..}{S} \;+\; :\overset{..}{O}:H^- \;\rightarrow\; :\overset{..}{O}:\overset{}{S}:\overset{..}{O}:H \quad\quad 4.14$$
$$\underset{..}{:O:} \quad\quad\quad\quad\quad \underset{..}{:O:}$$

giving $HSO_4{}^-$, hydrogen sulfate ion.

Electron pairs can also be donated into d orbitals, when these orbitals are available. For example, numerous compounds are known containing the complex hexafluorophosphate ion, $PF_6{}^-$. This ion is readily produced from

$$:\overset{..}{\underset{..}{F}}:{}^- \;+\; \overset{\overset{..}{\underset{..}{:F:}}}{\underset{\overset{..}{\underset{..}{F}}\;\;\overset{..}{\underset{..}{F}}}{\overset{..}{\underset{..}{:F:}}\;P\;\overset{..}{\underset{..}{:F:}}} \;\rightarrow\; \overset{\overset{..}{F}\;\;\overset{..}{F}}{\underset{\overset{..}{F}\;\;\overset{..}{F}}{:\overset{..}{\underset{..}{F}}:\;P\;:\overset{..}{\underset{..}{F}}:}} \quad\quad 4.15$$

Here the sixth bond was produced using a lone fluoride electron pair and a d orbital on phosphorus. In the $PF_6{}^-$ ion all orbitals available to phosphorus are used.

Odd Electron Molecules. In chemical reactions the bond forming process occurs in steps. In the over-all reaction represented by Eq. 4.10 the coming together at the same time of two hydrogen atoms and one oxygen atom would indeed be a most unlikely occurrence. Thus, in a reaction involving atoms of hydrogen and oxygen, a species like $\cdot\overset{.}{\underset{..}{O}}:H$, hydroxyl radical, might be formed. The hydroxyl radical is an example of an odd electron molecule or free radical, so-called because of the presence of a single unpaired electron. Such molecules, as a rule, are extremely reactive because they can easily combine with each other or with other odd electron carriers, each contributing an electron and an orbital for overlap. The OH radical e.g. can react either with more hydrogen atoms or with other OH radicals.

$$H\cdot \;+\; \cdot\overset{..}{\underset{..}{O}}:H \;\rightarrow\; H:\overset{..}{\underset{..}{O}}:H \quad\quad 4.16$$

or

$$H : \overset{..}{\underset{..}{O}} \cdot \ + \ \cdot \overset{..}{\underset{..}{O}} : H \rightarrow H : \overset{..}{\underset{..}{O}} : \overset{..}{\underset{..}{O}} : H \qquad 4.17$$

In the latter case H_2O_2, hydrogen peroxide, is formed. An odd electron in a molecule thus represents a point of high reactivity. Because of this high reactivity, free radicals seldom have more than a fleeting existence at room temperature. The few instances of odd electron molecules which persist at room temperature include nitrogen (II) oxide, NO, nitrogen (IV) oxide or nitrogen dioxide, NO_2, and chlorine (IV) oxide or chlorine dioxide, ClO_2.

Free radicals, however, are often important intermediate products in chemical reactions. Very reactive free radicals can be produced in electric discharges through gases, by the action of radiation, or at high temperatures in flames. All these methods produce a situation of high energy, sufficient to break a covalent bond. Two radicals are then the temporary results

$$H : H + \text{ electric discharge } \rightarrow H \cdot \ + \ \cdot H \qquad 4.18$$

$$H : \overset{..}{\underset{..}{O}} : \overset{..}{\underset{..}{O}} : H + \text{ heat } \rightarrow H : \overset{..}{\underset{..}{O}} \cdot \ + \ \cdot \overset{..}{\underset{..}{O}} : H \qquad 4.19$$

Multiple Bonding. Sharing of electrons between atoms is not limited to single pairs. Two or three bonds may be formed between a pair of atoms. Multiple bonding may occur between like or different atoms and is limited again by the availability of orbitals and electrons.

$$:N :::N : \qquad\qquad :C :::N :^-$$
$$\text{nitrogen} \qquad\qquad \text{cyanide ion}$$

$$H : C :: \overset{..}{\underset{}{O}} : \qquad :\overset{..}{\underset{..}{O}} :: C :: \overset{..}{\underset{..}{O}} : \qquad :\overset{..}{\underset{..}{O}} :: N :: \overset{..}{\underset{..}{O}} :^+$$
$$\overset{}{\underset{}{H}}$$
$$\text{formaldehyde} \qquad\qquad \text{carbon dioxide} \qquad\qquad \text{nitronium ion}$$

$$:\ddot{O}::\ddot{S}:\ddot{O}: \qquad\qquad :\ddot{Cl}:\\ :\ddot{Cl}:\ddot{P}::\ddot{O}:\\ :\ddot{Cl}:$$

sulfur dioxide   phosphorus oxychloride

For instance, the triple bond in cyanide ion uses three electron pairs accommodated by overlap of three carbon and three nitrogen orbitals. There remains one orbital on each of the atoms. There are ten electrons total, composed of four from carbon, five from nitrogen and an extra electron giving the molecule a net -1 charge. After the six bonding electrons have been accommodated, the remaining four fit neatly in pairs into the remaining two atomic orbitals. Cyanide ion is a quite stable entity with respect to the neutral CN radical with one less electron. One might suspect that this is due to the fact that the additional electron can easily be accommodated in the partially filled carbon orbital.

$$e^- + \cdot C:::N: \rightarrow :C:::N:^- \qquad\qquad 4.20$$

The process releases energy because the added electron is attracted to the carbon atom.

In the heavier elements, *d* orbitals may also be used. This is illustrated by the last formula above, representing phosphorus oxychloride. Since there are five electron pairs around phosphorus, one extra *d* orbital on phosphorus is used beyond the four *s* and *p* orbitals.

Three is the maximum number of bonds that can be formed between two atoms. This limitation is caused by the geometry of orbitals used in bonding and will be discussed later.

Formal Charge. Electronic dot formulas essentially convey our notions of how electrons are paired up in molecules. Taking the simplest view, i.e., that an electron-pair bond implies equal sharing of the electron pair between the bonded atoms, one can place a second interpretation on these formulas. This interpretation concerns the distribution of charges in molecules. Consider, for instance, the ammonia molecule

$$H : \overset{..}{N} : H$$
$$H$$

If the three bonding electron pairs are equally shared between hydrogen and nitrogen, one can formally assign half of the charge in each bond to each atom. Thus, each hydrogen atom is assigned one electronic charge and the nitrogen atom three electronic charges plus two from the lone pair on nitrogen. On this basis, the atoms in the molecule would have effectively a share of electronic charge that is the same as in the separate neutral atoms, i.e., one for hydrogen and five for nitrogen. This is expressed by saying that the *formal charge* on all atoms in the molecule is zero.

Now take the addition compound of NH_3 and BF_3

$$\overset{\oplus H \quad F \ominus}{H : \overset{..}{N} : \overset{..}{B} : F}$$
$$H \quad F$$

Again, assume that each hydrogen atom has the equivalent of one electron, the same as in the free atom, and has a zero formal charge. The fluorine atoms get one electron from the bonding pair and six electrons from the three lone pairs for a total of seven, as in the fluorine atom, and again the formal charge is zero. But nitrogen in this compound formally has the equivalent of only four electrons, one less than in the neutral atom, and therefore is assigned a formal charge of $+1$, whereas boron with formally one more electron charge than in the three-electron boron atom carries a -1 formal charge. Since the molecule is neutral, the total formal charges add up to zero.

This picture has utility since it conveys the idea that the electron density on the nitrogen atom after addition compound formation is less than the electron density on the nitrogen atom in uncombined ammonia. One should be careful not to misinterpret the formal charge assignments. Where the dot formulas indicate formal charges the sharing of electrons usually is not on an equal basis, so that the actual net charge concentration is much less than indicated. In our example the original nitrogen lone pair most probably resides, on the average, more closely on the nitrogen atom than on the boron atom, so that the net charge on nitrogen is only a small fraction of a full positive charge.

Information of this sort is difficult to express within the limitations of a paper formula. This serves to emphasize that the dot formulas are relatively simple, but also quite imperfect representations of real molecules.

Polarity of Bonds

Unequal sharing of electrons in a covalent bond is by no means restricted to molecules where the dot structure would indicate formal charges. Take, for example, the hydrogen halides, HX, where X represents a halogen atom.

$$H : \overset{..}{\underset{..}{X}} :$$

In these molecules both atoms have zero formal charge, but the physical properties indicate that there are nevertheless small charges of opposite sign on the hydrogen and the halogen atom, respectively.

Dipole Moment. The evidence comes from an examination of the dielectric constant of the hydrogen halides. In an electric field, say between the plates of a condenser, molecules that have a charge separation within them will tend to orient themselves with the electric field. Such molecules behave like *electric dipoles* (Fig. 4.3) and are called *polar* molecules. The extent of orientation is reflected by a change in the dielectric

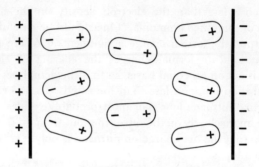

Fig. 4.3. Dipoles in a field.

constant, which can be measured from the change in capacitance of the condenser. Counteracting the orientation tendency is the thermal motion of the molecules. Since the average speed of the molecules depends on temperature, the change of dielectric constant with temperature allows deductions to be made about the strength of the molecular dipoles.

The strength of a dipole is measured by its dipole moment, μ, which is defined as the product of the magnitude of the charges and the distance between them.

$$\mu = \delta \cdot e \cdot d \qquad 4.21$$

e is the charge on an electron, 4.80×10^{-10} electrostatic units, and δ the fraction of electron charge that is separated.

Table 4.2 gives the dipole moments for the hydrogen halides.

TABLE 4.2. Dipole Moments of Hydrogen Halides

	Dipole Moment (10^{-18} esu)	Bond Distance (10^{-8} cm)	Fractional Electronic Charge
HF	1.91	0.92	0.43
HCl	1.03	1.27	0.17
HBr	0.78	1.41	0.12
HI	0.38	1.61	0.05

Since for these molecules the distances between atoms are known, the fractional charges can be calculated. It is seen that in HF there is the largest separation of charge, with a steady decrease in the series HF, HCl, HBr, HI.

The data can be interpreted by assuming that electrons are not shared equally between hydrogen and halogen. To be sure, the data by themselves do not show where the positive or the negative end of the dipole is, but the weight of other chemical evidence (e.g., tendency to form negative ions) indicates that the halogen atoms in each case constitute the negative end of the dipole. In this light the electrons are farthest displaced towards fluorine and least towards iodine in the HX molecules. This means that fluorine apparently is more effective in pulling electrons to itself than are the other halogens, and hydrogen less effective than any of the halogens.

Fig. 4.4 shows a representation of the hydrogen fluoride molecule as a dipole. The dipole moment is represented as an arrow, marking the positive end. Since the dipole moment

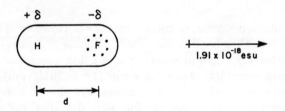

Fig. 4.4. Dipole moment.

has both magnitude and direction, it is a vector quantity　as are forces or velocities.

In diatomic molecules, where there is only one bond, one can associate the dipole moment of the molecule with a property of the bond, the bond moment. In polyatomic molecules, however, the molecular dipole moment is the result of the interplay of several bond moments. The individual bond moments add like vectors to produce as the resultant the molecular dipole moment. This is illustrated in Fig. 4.5 with water as an example. In the angular molecule,

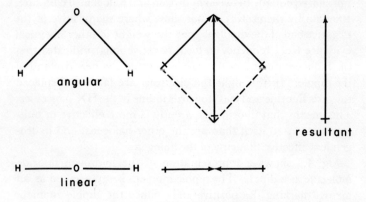

Fig. 4.5.   Addition of bond moments.

a resultant molecular moment is produced. However, if water were linear, the bond moments would oppose and cancel each other leaving a zero moment. The fact that water has a significant molecular dipole moment (1.8×10^{-18} esu) thus indicates not only that the electrons are shared unequally between hydrogen and oxygen, but also that the water molecule is not linear.

A more refined description of dipole moments would also have to consider that lone pairs may also contribute to the molecular moment. This becomes important when the lone pairs are in directed nonspherical orbitals. In such cases, the center of negative charge in the electron cloud and the center of positive charge, the nucleus, do not coincide. The result is that the molecule possesses a dipole moment. In some cases, the lone pair contribution to the dipole moment may be of considerable magnitude.

Electronegativity. Table 4.2 makes it apparent that atoms differ in their relative power of attraction for a shared electron pair, i.e., they have different electronegativities. One might ask which factors can explain the relative electron attracting power of atoms in *covalent bonds*.

One of the pertinent factors, the electron affinity, has already been discussed. The electron affinity represents the ability of an atom to accept electrons to form a negative ion. But in a covalent bond an atom not only accepts an electron from its partner but also gives up an electron to its partner, so that sharing is the result. The second factor influencing the electronegativity of an atom, then, is its ionization potential. The higher the ionization potential the more difficulty there is for electrons to be donated for equal sharing because of the energy which has to be supplied.

Relative electronegativities have been computed for the elements by taking an average of electron affinity and ionization potential. The values thus obtained are listed in Table 4.3. The trends in these values parallel more or less the trends

TABLE 4.3. Electronegativities

Li	Be	H	B	C	N	O	F
1.0	1.5	2.1	2.0	2.5	3.0	3.5	4.0
Na	Mg		Al	Si	P	S	Cl
0.9	1.2		1.5	1.8	2.1	2.5	3.0
K	Ca			Ge	As	Se	Br
0.8	1.0			1.8	2.0	2.4	2.8
Rb	Sr			Sn	Se	Te	I
0.8	1.0			1.8	1.9	2.1	2.5
Cs	Ba			Pb	Bi		
0.7	0.9			1.8	1.9		

in ionization potential. In a period there is a steady increase in electronegativity going from left to right whereas in a group there is a decrease from top to bottom. As with ionization potentials, the total change within a period is much greater than the change within a family group. Thus the most electronegative elements are found in the upper right corner of the periodic table, and the least electronegative ones to the lower left.

The calculated electronegativity values are in accord with chemical facts when one uses differences in electronegativity as the basis for comparison. Bonds where there is little or no difference in electronegativity are nonpolar and may be assumed to involve equal electron sharing. The larger the electronegativity difference is the more polar is the bond and the more charge separation there is in a given compound class.

Hydrogen compounds offer a good illustration. In HF, H_2O, and NH_3 strongly polar covalent bonds are produced with hydrogen carrying a partial positive charge. In CH_4 and BH_3, where the electronegativity difference between H and C or B has become smaller the molecules contain only slightly polar bonds, the partial charge on hydrogen reversing its sign between carbon and boron. However, in beryllium hydride, BeH_2, there are strongly polar bonds, hydrogen carrying a partial negative charge, and finally lithium hydride, LiH, is perhaps best described as an ionic solid containing negative hydride ion. In this last case the transfer of charge to the more electronegative atom is largely completed. The chemical reactions of this series of hydrogen compounds vary in a consistent fashion, too. Where hydrogen carries a partial negative charge according to electronegativity, reactions characteristic of negative hydrogen are often observed. Where the partial charge is positive, that is, when there is a relative deficiency of electrons on hydrogen, as in HF or H_2O, reactions usually remove protons without electrons, as would be expected.

Ionic vs. Covalent Bonding. The examples serve to illustrate an important point about the distinction between ionic and covalent bonding. The distinction is made on the basis of clear-cut examples that approach ideal situations. In reality, however, the distinctions are commonly not so clear, because one could identify the unequal sharing of electrons in polar bonds, where there is a partial charge transfer from one atom to the other, as an element of ionic bonding, where there is complete charge transfer. In this sense, polar bonds have a definite amount of ionic character.

The term "amount of ionic character" and its relation to electronegativity differences is not very well defined, in spite of many attempts to establish quantitative relations. For instance, calcium chloride with an electronegativity difference between Ca and Cl of 2.0 is certainly an ionic compound, yielding on melting a conducting liquid, while boron trifluoride, with the same electronegativity difference of 2.0 is a gas, does not conduct electricity when liquefied, and is best described as consisting of covalent molecules with polar bonds. Electronegativity differences are thus best used to describe qualitatively the change in bond character in a series of compounds where one of the atoms remains the same, as in the series of hydrogen compounds mentioned above.

In general, one may say that ionic bonding is favored by large electronegativity differences, making the fluorides the most ionic compounds in a series of analogous halides, oxides more ionic than sulfides, and so on. The elements on the left of the periodic table, being the least electronegative, do tend to form the most ionic compounds with the highly electronegative nonmetals on the right. Other factors that favor ionic character are: large size, low oxidation number, low actual or formal charge on the positive constituents, and small size in simple negative ions (Chapter 3). For instance, $TiCl_2$ and $TiCl_3$ are predominantly ionic, whereas $TiCl_4$ (high oxidation number or charge on Ti) is predominantly covalent, with distinct $TiCl_4$ molecules. Again, lead compounds, because of the large size of lead atoms, tend to be more ionic than the corresponding silicon compounds.

Variation in Effective Electronegativity. The electronegativities quoted in Table 4.3 are associated with combined atoms. The environment of atoms changes as different other atoms surround them in compounds. One therefore may expect that the electronegativity of an atom in molecules is not precisely constant if there are drastic changes in bonding, but may vary slightly to either side of the stated value. The factors that may change effective electronegativities are multiple bonds, change in coordination number, formal charges, and the character of adjacent atoms.

For instance, acetylene can react to lose a proton, whereas ethane reacts in this way only with extreme difficulty.

$$H : C \vdots\vdots\vdots C : H$$

acetylene

$$\begin{array}{cc} H & H \\ H : \overset{\cdot\cdot}{C} : \overset{\cdot\cdot}{C} : H \\ H & H \end{array}$$

ethane

One might interpret this fact by assuming that the presence of a triple bond effectively has increased the electronegativity of carbon. Again, a positive formal charge effectively increases the electronegativity of a bound atom because the extra charge will tend to pull electrons closer to it. Thus, the N—H bond in ammonium ion is more polar than the N—H bond in ammonia, because of the $+1$ formal charge on nitrogen.

$$\begin{array}{c} H \\ \overset{\cdot\cdot}{\underset{\oplus}{}} \\ H : \overset{..}{N} : H \\ H \end{array} \qquad\qquad \begin{array}{c} \overset{\cdot\cdot}{} \\ H : \overset{..}{N} : H \\ H \end{array}$$

As a result there is an increased partial positive charge on each of the four ammonium ion hydrogens. The operation of the formal charge effect thus can distribute the net plus charge of the ion over the periphery of the molecule rather than having it centered on the nitrogen atom.

The effect of adjacent atoms is illustrated by the difference in the compounds methanol, CH_3OH, and hypochlorous acid, ClOH.

$$
\begin{array}{cc}
\text{H} -\delta + \delta & -\delta + \delta \\
\text{H} : \ddot{\text{C}} : \ddot{\text{O}} : \text{H} \qquad & : \ddot{\text{Cl}} : \ddot{\text{O}} : \text{H} \\
\text{H} &
\end{array}
$$

On the face of it, both O—H bonds should be the same. But, substitution of a Cl atom for CH_3 in methanol results in a shift of electron density away from oxygen because of the larger electronegativity of chlorine than of the methyl carbon. This, in turn, produces an increased attraction for electrons in oxygen and in effect increases the electronegativity of the oxygen atom in this molecule. The oxygen-hydrogen bond thus becomes more polar, and hypochlorous acid donates H^+ more readily than does methanol. This indirect effect of differences in electronegativities of adjacent atoms is called an *inductive effect*. Inductive effects are quite commonly used in explaining differences in the stabilities and reactivities of series of related molecules.

Geometry of Molecules

The discussion of the geometry of molecules will be principally confined to two features: the distances between atoms, or bond lengths, and the directions in which atoms are bonded, or bond angles. Bond lengths and angles have been determined experimentally for a large number and variety of molecules by the use of the methods of X-ray and electron diffraction and specialized techniques of spectroscopy.

Covalent Radii. Just as with ionic bonds (Eq. 3.16), attempts have been made to express observed distances between covalently bonded atoms as the sum of two contributions, each term corresponding to the radius of one atom. The result of these efforts, a listing of covalent radii, is given in Table 4.4.

TABLE 4.4.   Covalent Radii

Single Bonds				
	B	C	N	O	F
	0.80	0.77	0.74	0.74	0.72 Å
H		Si	P	S	Cl
0.37		1.17	1.10	1.04	0.99
		Ge	As	Se	Br
		1.22	1.21	1.17	1.14
		Sn	Sb	Te	I
		1.40	1.41	1.37	1.33
Double Bonds				
		C	N	O	
		0.67	0.62	0.62	
			P	S	
			1.00	0.94	
Triple Bonds				
		C	N	
		0.60	0.55	

The covalent radii differ from ionic radii because the attractive and repulsive forces differ in the two kinds of bonds and therefore a different equilibrium internuclear distance (Fig. 3.1) will be achieved in the two cases. Nevertheless, the variation of covalent radii over the periodic table shows the same trends as the variation of ionic radii.

Going to the right in the periodic table, we find a decrease in covalent radius. This decrease can be attributed, as before, to the effect of increasing nuclear charge, which tends to pull together the outer electrons which are all in the same principal quantum number level. In a family the radii increase from period to period because now the overwhelming effect is the increase in total number of filled core levels which provide efficient screening of the nuclear charge and overpower the contracting effect of the atomic number increase.

For multiple bonds a different set of radii must be used because multiple bonds represent greater attractive forces between atoms than is true of single bonds. Consequently, atoms can approach each other more closely before repulsions cause an increase in energy. Multiple bond radii are therefore smaller than single bond radii.

The calculation of bond lengths by the use of the sum of covalent radii usually agrees well with observed distances. However, as is the case with other atomic parameters that are used for calculations on molecules, small discrepancies are sometimes observed. For instance, a considerable degree of ionic character in a covalent bond may decrease somewhat the bond distance so that the calculated value may be a little too large. Again, increase in coordination number may increase the bond distance beyond the calculated value. Finally, in some molecules, bonding is not satisfactorily accounted for by a single way of pairing up electrons. In such cases again the bond length differs from the calculated values. This subject will be more fully explored later in the discussion of resonance and electron delocalization.

Bond Angles. The angle between the directions of two bonds in a molecule is called the bond angle. Table 4.5 lists bond angles for a number of different neutral molecules and molecular ions. The examples are grouped into categories with similar bond angles. What other similarities are there between molecular species that have similar bond angles?

The most apparent similarity within each group is in the electronic dot formulas for the molecules. Insofar as the formulas represent a picture of electron distribution a bonding electron pair is concentrated most strongly in the direction

TABLE 4.5   Bond Angles in Some Molecules

Four Directions			Three Directions		
Species	Angle		Species	Angle	
CH_4	HCH	109°	BF_3	FBF	120°
NH_4	HNH	109°	SO_3	OSO	120°
BF_4^-	FBF	109°	NO_3^-	ONO	120°
NH_3	HNH	107°	NOCl	ClNO	116°
N_2H_4	HNN	108°	CH_3NO_2	CNO	116°
H_2O	HOH	105°		ONO	128°
$POCl_3$	ClPCl	106°	H_2CO	HCH	119°

Two Directions			Six Directions		
Species	Angle		Species	Angle	
CO_2	OCO	180°	SF_6	FSF	90°
HCN	HCN	180°	PCl_6^-	ClPCl	90°
$Hg(CH_3)_2$	CHgC	180°			

of the line joining the bonded atoms. In multiple bonds more than one pair lies predominantly in this direction. Unshared pairs inasmuch as they occupy directed orbitals are concentrated along the direction of the orbital.

For instance, in Table 4.5, under the heading "two directions" all the formulas indicate electrons being concentrated in two directions from the underlined atom. In CO_2 there

$$:\ddot{O}::C::\ddot{O}: \qquad\qquad H:C:::N \qquad\qquad H_3C:Hg:CH_3$$

are two pairs in each of the directions, in HCN, one pair and three pairs, and in mercury dimethyl, $Hg(CH_3)_2$, one pair in each direction. All these molecules are linear about the underlined atom, i.e., the bond angle is 180°.

Under the heading "four directions" the dot formulas all imply concentration of electrons in four directions about the central atom, each pair or pairs in a separate bond and each

$$\begin{array}{ccc}
H & H & :\ddot{C}l: \\
H:\ddot{C}:H & H:\ddot{N}:\ddot{N}:H & :Cl:\ddot{P}::\ddot{O}: \\
\ddot{H} & \ddot{H} & :\ddot{C}l:
\end{array}$$

lone pair accounting for one direction. The same similarity is noted when the dot formulas are written for the other groups.

TABLE 4.6. Geometry of Electron Pairs

No. of Charge Concentrations	Arrangement	Angle for Minimum Repulsion	Hybridization
2	linear	180°	sp
3	trigonal planar	120°	sp^2
4	tetrahedral	109°	sp^3
5	trigonal bipyramidal	90° 120°	dsp^3
6	octahedral	90°	d^2sp^3

Electrostatic Model. A simple model that can account for the observed bond angles in a qualitative way comes from a consideration of electrostatic repulsions of electron pairs. Let us consider electron pairs around an atom as concentrations of charge placed on a more or less spherical surface, and let us assume that the electrons can move in pairs. Barring other forces, the most likely arrangement will be the one where the electron pairs exert the minimum repulsion on each other. This will be achieved when the electrons get as far away from each other as possible. Since the electrons are restricted by our assumption to a sphere, the maximum distance of separation corresponds to a maximum angle between their positions and the center of the sphere.

It is easy to show by solid geometry and Coulomb's law that two charges would tend to move to opposite positions on a sphere, at an angle of 180° to each other. Likewise, three **equal charges would tend** to move into the equatorial plane and be at 120° to each other, thus being at the corners of a trigonal plane. Table 4.6 lists the expected configurations on the basis of this model, with the angles, and Fig. 4.6 illustrates the pertinent geometrical figures and the directions of expected charge distribution. Among these geometries the trigonal

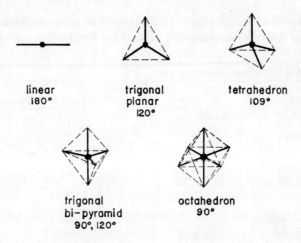

Fig. 4.6. Geometry of electron pair distributions.

bipyramidal one is the only one where the corner points are
not equidistant. It is not possible geometrically to arrange five
points equidistant on a sphere.

The different molecular configurations that can arise from
a particular basic geometry, tetrahedral in this case, are
illustrated in Fig. 4.7. A pertinent series of molecules would
be the series of ClO_4^-, ClO_3^-, and ClO_2^-. Perchlorate ion,

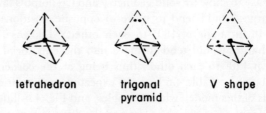

Fig. 4.7. Possible molecular shapes.

ClO_4^-, is clearly *tetrahedral*. Leaving out the lone pair in ClO_3^-, we see that the oxygen atoms define the base and Cl the apex of a *trigonal pyramid*. Finally ClO_2^-, chlorite ion, is *V-shaped*.

Comparison of the data in Table 4.5 with the predictions in Table 4.6 show quite gratifying agreement with a few small deviations. On inspection it is found that the deviations occur in molecules with lone pairs or with multiple bonds and can be explained qualitatively in a logical fashion. A lone pair can be expected to have its center of charge closer to the atom it resides on than can a bonding pair because a lone pair lacks the outward pull of the other bonded atom. If so, a lone pair would exert a greater repulsion on other charges than would a bonding pair. A lone pair thus tends to "push" bonding pairs closer together and tends to decrease the angles between bonds. This indeed is the case in the examples NH_3, N_2H_4, H_2O, and NCCl.

Multiple bonds represent regions in space with a rather high density of charge because of the additional electron pairs and therefore should also cause larger repulsions than a single bond. This would increase the angle between multiple bonds and single bonds and serve to compress the other single bond angles in the system. Examples of this are $POCl_3$ and H_2CO.

In nitro methane, CH_3NO_2, the two N—O bonds both have multiple bond character, as will be explained later. This causes the ONO angle to open up relative to a single bond angle causing the CNO angle to decrease.

The only examples of molecular geometries not explicitly covered by this model are square planar arrangements, where a central atom is surrounded by four other atoms or groups, all in a plane. Complex ions of Cu, Pd and Pt, like $Cu(NH_3)_4^{+2}$, are examples. Here the situation is complicated by the particular arrangement of *d* electrons. But in $Cu(NH_3)_4^{+2}$ in water solution there is evidence that the ion is actually a distorted octahedron with two additional water molecules above and below the square plane and at a fairly large distance from it (Fig. 4.8).

Molecular geometries are thus satisfactorily accounted for with this simple electrostatic model on the basis of a few ideal configurations which may be distorted slightly.

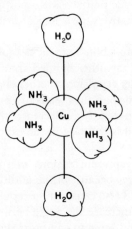

Fig. 4.8.   "Square planar $Cu(NH_3)_4^{++}$" —.
Actually octahedral $Cu(NH_3)_4^{++} \cdot 2H_2O$.

Hybridization. A satisfactory description of covalent bonding should also be able to account for molecular geometry, that is, for the mutual directions of bonds. Let us take for an example boron trifluoride, which is a trigonal planar molecule. Boron uses three orbitals to form three completely equivalent bonds to fluorine atoms.

Since boron has one *s* and three *p* orbitals available, we must now make a choice of three of these. From the three *p* orbitals indeed three equivalent bonds could be formed. But since p orbitals have their directions of maximum extension mutually at right angles, maximum overlap and strongest bonding would occur if the B—F bonds also would be at right angles to each other, forming a pyramidal molecule with boron at the apex. This prediction does not agree with the observed fact that boron trifluoride is a planar molecule. If one s and two p orbitals were used the bonds indeed would lie all in the plane defined by the two p orbitals, but the bond in overlap with an s orbital would be different, and in fact weaker, because of the smaller extension of the orbital in space. Consequently, one cannot describe adequately the observed geometry of BF_3 by the use of simple atomic orbitals.

The quandary, fortunately, can be resolved in a straightforward manner through the concept of *hybridization*. Three electrons in one s and two p orbitals represent a certain electron distribution over the boron atom.

This electron distribution and the corresponding energy are characteristic of a boron atom in an excited state $(2s2p_x2p_y)$, in which it is ready to form three covalent bonds with three unpaired electrons. It is important to realize that we are talking here about the *over-all* electron distribution resulting from the *superposition* of a $2s$, and two separate $2p$ electron clouds, and not necessarily about the individual electron clouds. The description of this excited state of boron in terms of electrons residing in distinct s and p orbitals is merely one of many ways of thinking about portions of the total electron distribution. Alternative descriptions are possible and these descriptions will be just as valid as the first, as long as they make use of three electrons and as long as the over-all electron distribution is the same. This point of view is justified because it is impossible to observe an individual electron in a boron atom and tell which orbital it occupies.

Instead of mentally subdividing the total electron cloud into three parts of equal charge, but different shapes, i.e., into half-

filled $2s$, $2p_x$ and $2p_y$ orbitals, one could attempt to get a subdivision into three portions which also have the same shape.
In solving this problem, we should remember that atomic orbitals are mathematical expressions and that there will be a
mathematical procedure which corresponds to the process of
subdivision. Perhaps an analogy (not to be carried too far)
will clear up this point. An apple is often thought of as consisting of the skin, the core, and the meat of the fruit, and, indeed, this is also the way apples are often divided into portions.
But there is nothing to prevent us from dividing the apple into
three similar segments, each segment containing one-third of
the skin, one-third of the core, and one-third of the meat.

Similarly, in the atomic case of the excited boron atom
where one s and two p orbitals are filled, it is possible to divide
the total electron distribution into three portions, each portion
representing a mixture of the s orbital and the two p orbitals.
The result is a set of three new orbitals, called *hybrid orbitals*
and symbolized by the designation sp^2 to indicate the kind
and the number of the component atomic orbitals. The three
sp^2 hybrid orbitals may be made equivalent to one another if
one makes sure that each orbital contains one-third of the s
orbital, the remaining two-thirds being made up of p orbitals.
There are mathematical rules based on modern quantum
theory which must be satisfied in this calculation, so that the
mixing is not arbitrary. Fig. 4.9 gives a pictorial analogy to
the mathematical mixing process.

As shown in Fig. 4.9 the hybrid sp^2 orbitals all have basi-
cally the same shape. They are much more concentrated into
regions that are in specific directions in space than are the
simple atomic orbitals. For instance, simple atomic p orbitals
have two regions in space, in opposite directions from the nucleus and located where the orbital would give a sizable electron density (Fig. 2.6). In the sp^2 orbitals, one of these regions
has shrunk to a rather small size while the region in the oppo-

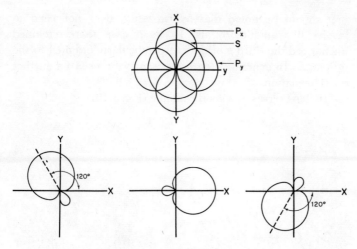

Fig. 4.9. Hybrid sp^2 orbitals.

site direction has expanded, so that now the electron density is primarily in this latter region. Finally, the directions of maximum extension in space of the hybrid orbitals are at angles of 120° to one another, and the directions of maximum extension are all in one plane. This last fact can be demonstrated quite easily by the application of solid geometry.

In boron trifluoride, each of the boron-to-fluorine bonds would be formed by the overlap of a boron sp^2 orbital with a fluorine orbital. Since maximum overlap, giving the strongest bond (p. 63), would occur in the direction where the hybrid orbital has its longest extension, the angle between two B—F bonds is determined by the angle between two sp^2 orbitals giving finally a planar molecule with 120° bond angles. Further, since all three sp^2 orbitals have the same shape, the strength of the bonds using any of them will be the same. Thus all three B—F bonds are equivalent. In this fashion the main features of the molecular geometry are accounted for in a natural way by the use of the hybrid orbital concept.

It should be noted that hybridization does not need to involve all available orbitals. In the sp^2 case, there remained unchanged the third p orbital perpendicularly oriented to the sp^2 plane. In general, such orbitals may be used for further bond formation.

Ethylene serves as a good example (Fig. 4.10).

$$H : \underset{\displaystyle H}{C} : : \underset{\displaystyle H}{C} : H$$

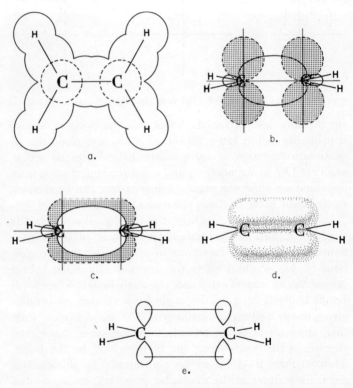

Fig. 4.10. σ and π bonding in ethylene

The bond angles in ethylene are 120°, and the hybridization on carbon is sp^2, as in BF_3. Each carbon atom forms two bonds to the two hydrogen atoms and one bond to the other carbon atom, and so uses all three sp^2 orbitals. There remains on each carbon atom one p orbital perpendicular to the plane of the C—H and C—C bonds. The second bond between the carbon atoms can be formed with these two orbitals and the remaining two electrons. The overlap between the p-orbitals is different in the second bond because it will have to occur "sideways."

Boron trifluoride and ethylene are but two of the many instances where the directional properties of covalent bonds are better described in terms of overlap of hybrid orbitals than in terms of simple atomic orbitals.

Let us consider, for example, the relation between the geometry and the covalent bond description for a molecule of hydrogen cyanide, HCN (a deadly poisonous gas, by the way). The dot formula for this molecule

$$H:C:::N:$$

indicates two directions of concentration of electron density around carbon, and our electrostatic model would predict a bond angle of 180° for the H—C—N arrangement. This is indeed the bond angle determined by experiment.

To explain the bonding there would be two orbitals needed in carbon which should be concentrated strongly in opposite directions so that maximum overlap for the two bonds to hydrogen and to nitrogen would occur at an angle of 180°. On mathematical analysis of the problem it is found that one s and one p orbital can be hybridized to form two new hybrid orbitals, sp orbitals, to fulfill this requirement. Each new orbital is a mixture of one-half of an s orbital and one-half of a p orbital. The situation on nitrogen is quite similar, only here the second orbital would not be used in bond formation but would hold the lone pair.

The formation of hybrid orbitals suitable for bonding at the expected angles leaves over two p orbitals on carbon, at right angles to each other and to the sp direction. Similarly, two p orbitals are left over on nitrogen and the remaining four electrons can just be accommodated in two sets of two p orbitals, overlapping sideways, as in ethylene. Thus three bonds are formed between carbon and nitrogen, but only one of these involved direct overlap and hybrid orbitals.

In addition to the two types of hybrid orbitals (sp and sp^2) discussed so far, there are a number of others, representing different mixtures of atomic orbitals, that are commonly used in the description of directed covalent bonding. For example, one s and three p orbitals will lead to a set of four sp^3 hybrid orbitals; two d orbitals, one s orbital, and three p orbitals give a set of six d^2sp^3 orbitals. The general rule here is as follows: (1) the number of hybrid orbitals present will be the same as the number of atomic orbitals used in their construction, and (2) hybrid orbitals of one kind differ from one another by and large only in their direction in space.

There is no way to predict off-hand the angles between a set of hybrid orbitals without elaborate mathematical calculations, so the geometry of the orbitals is a matter that the beginner simply has to remember. The important distinction between simple atomic and hybrid orbitals lies in the fact that hybrid orbitals are much more concentrated into one direction in space than are atomic orbitals, and they have a different geometrical relation to one another. Table 4.7 lists various hybrid orbitals and their general geometries. The numbers listed in the table under overlap strength provide a measure of the relative concentration of the orbitals into one direction.

Table 4.8 gives examples of hybridization in a number of molecules and ions. It will be instructive to write the dot formulas for some of the examples and observe the relation between the type of hybridization and the bond angles given in Table 4.5.

TABLE 4.7. Hybrid Orbitals

Orbital	Number of Orbitals	Geometry	Overlap Strength
sp	2	linear	1.932
sp^2	3	planar, 120°	1.991
sp^3	4	tetrahedral	2.000
dsp^2	4	square planar	2.694
dsp^3	5	trigonal bipyramidal	varies
d^2sp^3	6	octahedral	2.923
s	1	---	1.000
p	3	---	1.732

σ *and* π *Bonds.* In ethylene (Fig. 4.10) one can distinguish two kinds of bonds that differ in the symmetry of the resulting electron distribution. In the single bonds direct overlap produces an electron cloud that is cylindrically symmetrical with respect to the bond direction as an axis. That means that in a cross section through the electron cloud perpendicular to the bond direction, points of equal electron density lie on a circle. This type of bond is called a *sigma bond*, using the greek letter σ for short. The "sideways" overlap produces an electron cloud that has a plane of symmetry that lies in the bond direction. The electron cloud above that plane is a reflection of the cloud below the plane. There is zero probability for electrons to be in that plane, just as for the constituent p

TABLE 4.8. Hybridization in Some Common Chemical Species*

sp	$\underline{C}O$, $\underline{C}O_2$, $\underline{C}_2H_2$, $\underline{N}_2$, $HC\underline{N}$, $\underline{C}N^-$, $\underline{N}_3^-$
sp^2	$\underline{S}O_3$, $\underline{S}O_2$, $\underline{B}Cl_3$, $\underline{C}_2H_4$, $H_2\underline{C}O$, $\underline{C}H_3^+$, $\underline{C}H_3COOH$, $\underline{N}O_3^-$, $\underline{C}O_3^{--}$
sp^3	$\underline{N}H_3$, $\underline{N}H_4^+$, $\underline{C}H_4$, $\underline{C}H_3^-$, $\underline{C}_2H_6$, $\underline{C}lO_3^-$, $\underline{C}lO_4^-$, $\underline{B}F_4^-$, SO_4
dsp^3	$\underline{P}F_5$, $\underline{P}Cl_5$, $\underline{S}Cl_4$, $\underline{C}lF_3$
d^2sp^3	$\underline{P}F_6^-$, $\underline{S}F_6$, $\underline{A}lF_6^{--}$, $H_5\underline{I}O_6$

*For the underlined atoms.

orbitals. Such a bond is called a *pi bond*, designated by the symbol π. In ethylene, then, the hydrogen atoms are bonded by σ bonds and the carbon atoms by a σ and a π bond. The bond strength for C—C is about 83 kcal/mole, and for C=C 146 kcal/mole, less than twice the C—C strength. It appears that the energy lowering resulting from the additional π bond is not as great as that due to the first bond. This might be caused by the lesser overlap in the π bond. In general then, the first bond between two atoms will always be a σ bond.

Restricted Rotation. A little reflection will reveal that maximum overlap in a π bond is produced when the p orbitals are parallel to each other, and any rotation of these orbitals about the bond direction would decrease overlap. Since the directions of the p orbitals are fixed at right angles with respect to the σ bond planes, the most stable configuration of ethylene with maximum π overlap is achieved when the σ bond planes coincide; in other words, all the atoms in the molecule should be in one plane. This is indeed true in ethylene, and experiments indicate that rotation of the two CH_2 halves about the C=C bond results in an increase in potential energy. There is *restricted rotation* in ethylene. Rotation about pure σ bonds is not restricted in this way.

The planar geometry and restricted rotation in an ethylene-like compound makes possible the stable existence of *geometric isomers*. These are compounds that have the same formula and the same type of bonds but differ in the geometric arrangement of the bonds. The two isomers cannot be converted into each

cis-dichloroethylene   *trans*-dichloroethylene

other easily because rotation about the double bond is hindered.

Limit to Multiple Bonding. The distinction between σ and π bonds makes apparent the limitations to the number of bonds that may be formed at one time between two atoms. Only one σ bond can be formed because a second bond would have to place electrons into the space that is already densely populated by the first. But two π bonds are possible since the second bond could place its electrons into the region that is left sparsely occupied by the first, i.e., by overlap of p orbitals at right angles to the first set. Thereafter, the bonding region essentially is saturated with electrons, and what is more, no orbitals with proper symmetry are left. The total number of bonds between a pair of atoms is limited to a maximum of three.

Resonance and Electron Delocalization

The discussion of electron pairing and the description in terms of dot formulas has by and large been restricted to examples where it was possible to arrive at a unique way of pairing and sharing of electrons. This is not always the case.

Resonance. Consider the dot formulas for the nitrate ion. One may think of several ways of pairing up the twenty-four electrons in this ion. The formulas with formal charges are given below.

       I   II   III

These formulas are equivalent in that the same number of bonds are shown and the same general planar geometry would be predicted, but in each one a different oxygen atom is double bonded. There is really no basis for thinking that one of these formulas is a better representation for nitrate ion than the other. In fact, neither formula is adequate because all the oxygen atoms are chemically equivalent in

NO_3^-, whereas the formulas have one atom different from the other two.

One either has to reject the use of dot formulas in representing important features of molecular structure or one may attempt to change their meaning so that the observed equivalence of oxygen atoms in nitrate ion still can be described. In view of the otherwise great utility of the dot representation, the latter course is often followed.

One can still retain the dot forumlas if one takes the view that a) each formula represents only some aspect or feature of the nitrate ion structure and b) the superposition of these features gives a correct idea of the nitrate ion. If each of the formulas I, II and III carries equal weight, then a given nitrogen-oxygen bond would have effectively one third double bond character, since only in one of the three formulas is there a double bond to the oxygen atom. Also, a given oxygen atom would carry a formal charge of two thirds, since two out of the three formulas show a negative formal charge in this atom. Nitrogen would have a $+1$ formal charge since all formulas assign this charge. This view does make all the oxygen atoms alike, and would predict that the N—O bond distances are intermediate between those expected for single or double bonding. This is indeed true in nitrates.

Resonance is the description of the electronic structure of molecules by means of several schemes of pairing electrons (dot formulas), with features of each scheme contributing to the final description. The individual pairing models are called resonance structures. The resonance structures are but partial concepts of the molecules and have physical meaning only in combination with all the other pertinent resonance structures. For nitrate ion we could then write:

indicating the bonds by lines and the necessity of considering all three resonance structures by the connecting arrows.

Electron Delocalization. It will be instructive to look at a pictorial representation of the expected electron distribution in NO_3^-, as shown in Fig. 4.11. The first three pictures

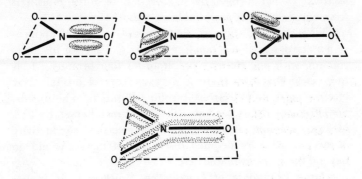

Fig. 4.11.   Electron delocalization in NO_3^-.

represent the electron clouds for the resonance structures and have no direct physical significance. The result of the super-position represents the molecule and indicates that the electron pair in the π bond is not restricted to one N—O region but is free to move all over the molecule; the electron pair is not localized in one bond, but delocalized over the three bonds. Delocalization is the natural consequence of more than one way of pairing electrons.

One might ask what the general conditions are for de-localization. Let us consider the situation in NO_3^- again. After the three σ bonds have been formed and two lone electron pairs have been localized on each oxygen, there remain on each atom one empty p orbital perpendicular to the plane of the molecule, for a total of four orbitals. There are also left three pairs of electrons, one less pair than there were orbitals. Whenever alternative electron pair structures can be written, it is found that there are more orbitals left than there are electron pairs, once the σ bonds and lone pairs have been assigned. Delocalization of the electrons over all the remaining orbitals then results. In this sense one may say that the electrons in NO_3^- are accommodated in *delocalized molecular orbitals* formed by the overlap of three p-orbitals from oxygen and one p-orbital from carbon.

This picture, by the way, finds a most important application in the description of bonding in metals. Take, for instance, sodium, with one electron per atom for four orbitals. It is quite clear that here there is a vast excess of orbitals over electron pairs, and electrons in solid sodium, as in all metals, are effectively delocalized over the whole metal crystal. This idea can account satisfactorily for the electrical conductivity of metals. A more detailed discussion of metals would go beyond the space available here.

Relative Importance of Contributing Structures.   It is not necessary for alternative electron dot formulas (pairing schemes) to be equivalent for consideration in the over-all combination. For example, one might consider a formula for NO_3^- where there are no multiple bonds.

The features of this resonance structure could be taken into consideration in the over-all description of the molecule, but it would not carry nearly the same weight as the previous resonance structures. For instance, in averaging the formal charges the $+2$ charge on nitrogen would not be taken as one out of four, but as much less than that.

There are quantitative mathematical techniques for proper weighting of nonequivalent contributions. Qualitatively, proposed pairing schemes would carry less weight when they show fewer bonds, when they have higher separation of formal charges, and if there are like formal charges on adjacent atoms. Usually it is sufficient to consider only the few most important structures, as was done for NO_3^-, in a description that adequately accounts for chemical behavior.

For instance, nitro methane could be represented by two formulas, omitting single bonded formulas.

$$H_3C-\overset{\oplus}{N}\overset{\ddot{O}:}{\underset{\underset{\ominus}{\ddot{O}:}}{\Big\|}} \qquad \longleftrightarrow \qquad H_3C-\overset{\oplus}{N}\overset{\overset{\ominus}{\ddot{O}:}}{\underset{\ddot{O}:}{\diagup}}$$

Since both formulas are equivalent, this would indicate a one-half double bond character in each $N-O$ link.

Carbon monoxide could be described by

$$:C::\overset{..}{O}: \quad \longleftrightarrow \quad \underset{\ominus}{:C:} \underset{\oplus}{:O:} \quad \longleftrightarrow \quad \underset{\ominus\ominus}{:\overset{..}{C}::O:} \underset{\oplus\oplus}{}$$

$$\text{I} \qquad\qquad\qquad \text{II} \qquad\qquad\qquad \text{III}$$

The first pairing scheme has the virtue of zero formal charges; the second one has unfavorable formal charges but this is compensated because there are three bonds; the last scheme is clearly less important than either of the first two: the high formal charges are not compensated by additional bonds. Carbon monoxide would in the main be described by a combination of the first two ways of electron pairing. Whether these pairing schemes carry equal weight or not cannot be decided. A quantitative calculation would have to be made. At any rate, one would expect considerable triple bond character in CO.

Energy Relations. It is often possible to account for the energy released in the formation of a molecule from atoms by assuming that the total energy is composed of separate contributions from each bond. Table 4.9 lists a few examples. When there is only one reasonable electron pair formula, the energies calculated in this way agree well with experimental determination, as in the case of propylene

$$
\begin{array}{ccc}
\text{H} & \text{H} & \text{H} \\
| & | & | \\
\text{H}-\text{C}=\text{C}-\text{C}-\text{H} \\
| & | & | \\
\text{H} & \text{H} & \text{H}
\end{array}
$$

where the total energy would be

$$ E = 8\,E_{C-H} + E_{C-C} + E_{C=C} $$

But in those instances where a unique bonding formula cannot be written, as in benzene,

$$
\begin{array}{c}
\text{H} \\
| \\
\text{C} \\
\text{H}-\text{C} \quad \text{C}-\text{H} \\
\text{H}-\text{C} \quad \text{C}-\text{H} \\
\text{C} \\
| \\
\text{H}
\end{array}
\quad\leftrightarrow\quad
\begin{array}{c}
\text{H} \\
| \\
\text{C} \\
\text{H}-\text{C} \quad \text{C}-\text{H} \\
\text{H}-\text{C} \quad \text{C}-\text{H} \\
\text{C} \\
| \\
\text{H}
\end{array}
$$

the energy calculated on the basis of one formula alone is too low by about 40 kcal/mole. This means that the delocalization of π electrons over all C—C bonds changes the bond energy enough to make the additivity rule invalid. The important point here is that whenever one can apply the resonance description the observed energy lowering on bonding is greater than predicted for just one pairing formula. The difference is termed *resonance energy* or *delocalization energy*. These energies are in a sense an expression of the error made in the description of the molecule by only one electron dot formula and using the bond energy additivity rule. Molecules for which the resonance description is important thus turn out to be more stable than suspected.

The increase in stability resulting from resonance or electron delocalization is important in the discussion of a great variety of chemical questions. A partial list of topics should stress this point. Properties of dyes, ultraviolet absorption, bond strengths, thermal stabilities, free radical reactions, heats of reaction, and rates of chemical reactions in general may be influenced by resonance stabilization in the chemical species involved.

TABLE 4.9. Bond Energies

	E(kcal/mole)		E(kcal/mole)
C—H	98.7		
C—O	85.5	C=O	176
C—C	82.6	C=C	145.8

SELECTED READINGS

1. Schroedinger, E., "What is Life and Other Scientific Essays," Doubleday Anchor Books, Garden City, N.Y., 1956.

   Nontechnical and searching essays on the philosophy of modern science by one of the pioneers; very readable.

2. Herzberg, G., "Atomic Spectra and Atomic Structure," 2nd ed., Dover Publications, New York, 1944.
3. Devault, D. J., "A Method of Teaching the Electronic Structure of the Atom." Journal of Chemical Education **21**, 575 (1944).
4. Keller, R. N. "Energy Level Diagrams and Extranuclear Building of the Elements." *J. Chem. Educ.* **39**, 289 (1962).

   The preceding three references give a good picture of the electronic structure of atoms.

5. Rice, O. K., "Electronic Structure and Chemical Binding," McGraw-Hill Book Co., Inc., New York, 1940.

   The chapter on the ionic bond is especially worthwhile.

6. Wells, A. F., "Structural Inorganic Chemistry," 3rd ed., Oxford University Press, 1961.

   Excellent source for the facts of molecular and crystal geometry; detailed discussions.

7. Waddington, T. C., "Lattice Energies and Their Significance in Inorganic Chemistry" *in* "Advances in Inorganic Chemistry and Radiochemistry." vol. 1, Academic Press, Inc., New York, 1959.

Simple and more advanced calculations of lattice energies; many applications.

8. Coulson, C. A., "Valence," Oxford University Press, 1952.
9. Pauling, L., "The Nature of the Chemical Bond," 3rd ed., Cornell University Press, Ithaca, N.Y., 1960.
10. Cartmell, E., and Fowles, G. W. A., "Valency and Molecular Structure," Academic Press, Inc., New York, 1956.

These three books are general references on modern theories of the covalent bond.

11. Noller, C. R. "A Physical Picture of Covalent Bonding and Resonance in Organic Chemistry," *J. Chem. Educ.* **27**, 504 (1950).

A very clearly written article.

12. Gillespie, R. J. and Nyholm, R. S. "Inorganic Stereochemistry." *Quart Revs London* **11**, 339 (1957).

The definitive article on the simple picture of molecular geometry.

13. Demitz, J. D., and Orgel, L. E., "Stereochemistry of Ionic Solids" *in* "Advances in Inorganic Chemistry and Radiochemistry," vol. 2, Academic Press, Inc., New York, 1960.

Mainly concerned with transition metal compounds.

14. Liehr, A. D., "Molecular Orbital, Valence Bond, and Ligand Field," *J. Chem. Educ.* **39**, 135 (1962).

An advanced supplement to reference 13; gives molecular energy level diagrams for different molecular geometries.

INDEX